Help yourself to
integration

 **LONGMAN**

Pearson Education Limited
Edinburgh Gate
Harlow
Essex
CM20 2JE
England and Associated Companies throughout the World

First published 1997
Second impression 2000
Printed in Singapore (KHL)

ISBN 0582 31804 1

The Publisher's policy is to use paper manufactured from sustainable forests.

Contents

Preface

The purpose of this book is to help to increase students' facility in integration.

There are plenty of exercises in this book. The exercises are graded, and most types of exercise have a worked example with a full commentary to provide assistance.

I would like to thank the authors of New General Mathematics, Messrs J B Channon, A McLeish Smith and H C Head, for allowing me to use their text for the sections on maxima and minima and for curve sketching, Rosemary Emanuel for checking the manuscripts and her many helpful suggestions, Sue Maunder for checking the answers and Addison Wesley Longman for their speed in producing this book.

The responsibility for any errors is mine.

Hugh Neill
March 22, 1997

1 How to use this book

Assumptions made

This is a book which is designed to help you to learn the integral calculus by giving you a number of carefully worked examples, and then problems based on them.

The assumption is that you are not a beginner, and that you have been taught some calculus already. Thus, no theory is given; if you need to know more, then you should consult your calculus book and your teacher.

At the beginning of each chapter, there is a list of work which you should have studied before commencing work.

Most of the techniques are introduced in the context of polynomials, so that the first six chapters contain most of the ideas and techniques for using integration. Chapters 7 to 10 are about methods of integration; in chapters 11 to 14 you can apply the techniques of the earlier part of the book in the context of more advanced functions.

Learning a technique

Suppose that you need to learn how to carry out a particular technique. Look for the chapter which includes the technique, check that you have covered the theory, and then study the worked examples carefully, preferably with a pen in your hand.

Write down the steps as you go, and check each step carefully. Ask yourself: Why was this particular step chosen? Do I agree with the working? Why is it like that?

Remember that mathematics is not disconnected, and if you can learn the general principles behind calculus, you will make better progress in other areas of the subject.

Trying the exercises

If you get stuck with a particular exercise, then look back at a worked example similar to the one you are having difficulty with, and try to isolate the place where you are having the problem.

Look at the answer. Sometimes, but not always, the general form of the answer can give you a clue. Remember that sometimes there can be different forms of the same answer, and it may be that your answer is correct, but you do not recognise it as such.

There are plenty of exercises in the book. Do as many as you need to perfect a technique.

Short cuts

In many cases the examples are worked in more detail than you need to give in a solution. If you can skip lines, go ahead; but don't make errors by doing so! It is better to write more steps, and to get the solution correct, than to skip steps, get things wrong and subsequently lose confidence.

Answers

Answers are given, but in some cases where the answer given may be in a form different from yours. If that is so, and you cannot reconcile your answer with that in the book, you should seek help.

2 Integrating powers and polynomials

You will need to know

- how to differentiate powers of x and polynomials usng the formula $y = kx^n$,

$$\frac{dy}{dx} = nkx^{n-1}$$

- the formula $\dfrac{x^{n+1}}{n+1} + C$, where C is a constant, for integrating x^n, $n \neq -1$.

You may find it helpful to think of the integration formula as, 'Raise the power by one, and divide by the new power'.

1 Find the functions which differentiate to give x^4, $3x^2$.

Use the $\dfrac{x^{n+1}}{n+1} + C$ rule with $n = 4$.	The required function is $\frac{1}{5}x^5 + C$.
Use the $\dfrac{x^{n+1}}{n+1}$ rule on x^2 with $n = 2$, and multiply the result by 3. Do not forget the constant.	The required function is $3 \times \frac{1}{3}x^3 + C$, or $x^3 + C$.

2 Integrate $\dfrac{1}{x^2}$, $4x^{-5}$, $\dfrac{3}{x^3}$.

Write $\dfrac{1}{x^2}$ as a power of x.	$\dfrac{1}{x^2} = x^{-2}$.
Use the $\dfrac{x^{n+1}}{n+1} + C$ rule with $n = -2$.	$\displaystyle\int x^{-2}\, dx = \dfrac{x^{-1}}{-1} + C$.
Simplify the result.	$\dfrac{x^{-1}}{-1} + C = -x^{-1} + C = -\dfrac{1}{x} + C$.

3

From this point onwards, the answers will usually be given in the $-x^{-1} + C$ form, rather than the $-\dfrac{1}{x} + C$ form.

3   Find $\displaystyle\int x^{\frac{3}{2}}\,dx$, $\displaystyle\int \sqrt{x}\,dx$, $\displaystyle\int \sqrt{\dfrac{2}{x}}\,dx$.

Use the $\dfrac{x^{n+1}}{n+1}$ rule on $x^{\frac{3}{2}}$ with $n = \frac{3}{2}$.

$$\int x^{\frac{3}{2}}\,dx = \frac{x^{\frac{5}{2}}}{\frac{5}{2}} + C$$

$$= \tfrac{2}{5} x^{\frac{5}{2}} + C.$$

To find $\displaystyle\int \sqrt{x}\,dx$ write $\sqrt{x}$ as a power of x. Then use the $\dfrac{x^{n+1}}{n+1}$ rule on $x^{\frac{1}{2}}$ with $n = \frac{1}{2}$.

$$\int \sqrt{x}\,dx = \int x^{\frac{1}{2}}\,dx$$

$$= \frac{x^{\frac{3}{2}}}{\frac{3}{2}} + C$$

$$= \tfrac{2}{3} x^{\frac{3}{2}} + C.$$

This integration shows the intermediate steps in detail.

$$\int \sqrt{\frac{2}{x}}\,dx = \sqrt{2}\int \sqrt{\frac{1}{x}}\,dx$$

$$= \sqrt{2}\int x^{-\frac{1}{2}}\,dx$$

$$= \sqrt{2} \times \frac{x^{\frac{1}{2}}}{\frac{1}{2}} + C$$

$$= 2\sqrt{2}\,x^{\frac{1}{2}} + C.$$

4   Find $\displaystyle\int \left(x^2 - 2x - 3\right)dx$.

You integrate a sum of functions by integrating them separately, then adding.

Use the $\dfrac{x^{n+1}}{n+1}$ rule on each term of the sum.

$$\int\left(x^2 - 2x - 3\right)dx$$
$$= \int x^2\,dx - 2\int x\,dx - 3\int 1\,dx$$
$$= \tfrac{1}{3}x^3 - 2\times\tfrac{1}{2}x^2 - 3\times x + C$$
$$= \tfrac{1}{3}x^3 - x^2 - 3x + C.$$

5 Find $\int\left(x^2 - 1\right)^2 dx$.

You cannot integrate this function as it stands, but you can carry out the squaring to get a polynomial function, which you can integrate.

Square $\left(x^2 - 1\right)$, and then integrate.

$$\int\left(x^2 - 1\right)^2 dx = \int\left(x^4 - 2x^2 + 1\right)dx$$
$$= \tfrac{1}{5}x^5 - \tfrac{2}{3}x^3 + x + C.$$

6 Find $\displaystyle\int\frac{x^4 + 1}{x^2}\,dx$.

As in Example 5, you cannot integrate this function as it stands, but you can divide to get a sum of functions, each of which you can integrate.

Divide $x^4 + 1$ by x^2 and then integrate.

$$\int\frac{x^4 + 1}{x^2}\,dx = \int\left(x^2 + \frac{1}{x^2}\right)dx$$
$$= \int x^2\,dx + \int x^{-2}\,dx$$
$$= \tfrac{1}{3}x^3 - x^{-1} + C.$$

In the worked examples, many steps have been put in, some of which you may wish to omit. This is fine, but when you have an integral always check by differentiation that it is correct. This is the basis of a method called 'Guess and check', which is very useful.

Exercise 2

Find the functions which differentiate to give the following functions.

1	x^2	**2**	$3x^2$
3	$5x^2$	**4**	x^4
5	$5x^4$	**6**	$3x^4$
7	x	**8**	$2x$
9	$3x$	**10**	5
11	$\frac{1}{2}x$	**12**	$\frac{1}{2}x^2$
13	$-\frac{1}{4}x^3$	**14**	$\frac{1}{x^2}$
15	$-\frac{2}{x^3}$	**16**	$\frac{1}{x^6}$

Find the following integrals.

17	$\int 3x^3\,dx$	**18**	$\int \frac{1}{3}x^3\,dx$
19	$\int \frac{3}{x^3}\,dx$	**20**	$\int -\frac{3}{x^4}\,dx$
21	$\int -\frac{2}{x^5}\,dx$	**22**	$\int 0\,dx$
23	$\int (4x-3)\,dx$	**24**	$\int (x+1)\,dx$
25	$\int (6x^2 - 2x + 1)\,dx$	**26**	$\int (2-6x)\,dx$
27	$\int (3x - x^2)\,dx$	**28**	$\int (9x^2 + 8)\,dx$
29	$\int \left(x^2 - \frac{1}{x^2}\right)dx$	**30**	$\int \left(x^3 + \frac{1}{x^3}\right)dx$
31	$\int (x^3 + x^2 + x + 1)\,dx$	**32**	$\int \left(\frac{1}{2}x^3 + \frac{1}{3}x^2 + \frac{1}{4}x + \frac{1}{5}\right)dx$
33	$\int (6x^5 - 4x^3 - 2x + 3)\,dx$	**34**	$\int \left(\frac{1}{2}x^3 - \frac{1}{3}x^2\right)dx$
35	$\int \left(\frac{2}{x^2} - \frac{5}{x^3}\right)dx$	**36**	$\int \left(\frac{5}{x^2} - \frac{6}{x^3} + \frac{6}{x^4}\right)dx$
37	$\int x^{\frac{1}{2}}\,dx$	**38**	$\int 2x^{\frac{1}{2}}\,dx$
39	$\int \frac{3}{2}x^{\frac{1}{2}}\,dx$	**40**	$\int -2x^{-\frac{1}{2}}\,dx$

41 $\int 2x^{\frac{2}{3}} \, dx$ **42** $\int 3x^{-\frac{2}{3}} \, dx$

43 $\int \sqrt{x} \, dx$ **44** $\int \frac{2}{\sqrt{x}} \, dx$

45 $\int 3\sqrt{x} \, dx$ **46** $\int \sqrt{3x} \, dx$

47 $\int \frac{2}{\sqrt{2x}} \, dx$ **48** $\int (x+2)^2 \, dx$

49 $\int (2x+3)(3x+2) \, dx$ **50** $\int \left(\sqrt{x} - \frac{1}{x}\right)^2 \, dx$

51 $\int (3x-1)(x+1) \, dx$ **52** $\int x^3(x+2) \, dx$

53 $\int \sqrt{x}(x+2) \, dx$ **54** $\int \sqrt{x}\left(\sqrt{x}+1\right)^2 \, dx$

55 $\int \frac{\left(\sqrt{x}+1\right)^2}{\sqrt{x}} \, dx$ **56** $\int \frac{x^3+1}{x^2} \, dx$

57 $\int \frac{(x+1)(x+2)}{x^4} \, dx$ **58** $\int \frac{(2x+1)(2x-1)}{\sqrt{x}} \, dx$

59 $\int \frac{2x^{\frac{1}{2}}+4x^{\frac{3}{2}}}{x^2} \, dx$ **60** $\int \frac{(2x)^{\frac{1}{2}}+(4x)^{\frac{3}{2}}}{x^3} \, dx$

3   Finding the constant

You will need to know

- how to integrate powers and polynomials
- how to use given information to find the value of the constant of integration.

1 The variables p and q are related by the equation $\dfrac{dp}{dq} = 2q + 4$. When $q = -2$, $p = 3$. Find the relation between p and q.

The equation $\dfrac{dp}{dq} = 2q + 4$ is an example of a differential equation, which are treated in more detail in Chapters 13 and 14. In the examples in this chapter you can solve the differential equation directly.

Integrate $\dfrac{dp}{dq} = 2q + 4$.	If $\dfrac{dp}{dq} = 2q + 4$ $p = q^2 + 4q + C$.
Substitute $q = -2$, $p = 3$ to find C.	When $q = -2$, $p = 3$, so $3 = (-2)^2 + 4 \times (-2) + C$ $\qquad = 4 - 8 + C$ $\qquad = -4 + C$ so $C = 7$.
Present the result.	The relation is $p = q^2 + 4q + 7$.

2 The gradient at any point of a curve is given by $\dfrac{dy}{dx} = 6x^2 + 10x - 7$. The curve passes through the point $(-3, 7)$. Find the equation of the curve.

Integrate $\dfrac{dy}{dx} = 6x^2 + 10x - 7$.	If $\dfrac{dy}{dx} = 6x^2 + 10x - 7$ $y = 2x^3 + 5x^2 - 7x + C$.
But $(-3, 7)$ satisfies this equation, so substitute $x = -3$, $y = 7$ to find C.	$(-3, 7)$ lies on the curve, so $7 = 2 \times (-3)^3 + 5 \times (-3)^2 - 7 \times (-3) + C$ $\quad = -54 + 45 + 21 + C$ $\quad = 12 + C$ so $C = -5$.
Present the result.	The equation is $y = 2x^3 + 5x^2 - 7x - 5$.

3 A straight line with gradient 2 passes through the point $(1, 3)$. Find the equation of the line.

Use the fact that gradient $= \dfrac{dy}{dx}$, and integrate.	If gradient $= 2$, then $\dfrac{dy}{dx} = 2$, so $y = 2x + C$.
But $(1, 3)$ satisfies this equation, so substitute $x = 1$, $y = 3$ to find C.	$(1, 3)$ lies on the line, so $3 = 2 \times 1 + C$ $\quad = 2 + C$ so $C = 1$.
Present the result.	The equation is $y = 2x + 1$.

Exercise 3

1 If u and v are two variables such that $\dfrac{du}{dv} = 4v - 3$, and $u = 5$ when $v = 2$, find u in terms of v.

2 Find the equation of the curve whose gradient is given by $2x + 3$, and which passes through the point $(2, 3)$.

3 Find the equation of the line with gradient 3 which passes through the point $(-1,4)$.

4 Two variables w and u are such that $\dfrac{dw}{du} = 9u^2 + 6u - 3$. If $w = -16$ when $u = -3$ find w in terms of u.

5 A line passes through the point $(5,-2)$, and its gradient is -3. Find the equation of the line.

6 A curve passes through the point $(4,-3)$, and its gradient is given by $2 - x$. Find the equation of the curve.

7 The point $(2,8)$ lies on a curve whose gradient at any point is given by $3x + 6$. Find the coordinates of the point on the curve at which the gradient is zero.

8 The gradient of a curve at any point is given by $x^2 - 2$. Find the equation of the curve, given that the point $(-1,3)$ lies on it.

9 A curve passes through the point $(1,3)$, and its gradient at any point on it is given by $2x - \dfrac{1}{x^2}$. Find the equation of the curve.

10 The gradient of a curve at any point is $5 - 6x$. Find the equation of the curve if it passes through the point $(1,2)$.

11 Find the equation of the curve which passes through the point $(2,-8)$, and whose gradient at any point is given by $3x^2 - 6x - 2$.

12 If a curve passes through the point $(-1,4)$, and its gradient at any point is $2x - 1$, find the coordinates of the point on the curve at which the gradient is -7.

13 A curve passes through the point $(2,7)$, and its gradient is given by $3 + 8x - 6x^2$. Find the equation of the curve.

14 A curve passes through the point $(-4,-6)$, and its gradient is given by $2x + 3$. Find the points where the curve crosses the x-axis.

15 The gradient of a curve is given by $3x^2 - 4x + \dfrac{2}{x^2}$. Find the equation of the curve if the point $(2,-4)$ lies on it.

16 A curve for which $\dfrac{dy}{dx} = 3\sqrt{x}$ passes through the point $(4,6)$. Find its equation.

4   Kinematics

You will need to know that, if s, v and a stand for displacement, velocity and acceleration, then

- $v = \dfrac{ds}{dt}$, so $s = \int v\,dt$

- $a = \dfrac{dv}{dt}$, so $v = \int a\,dt$.

1   A particle moves in a straight line, and its velocity after t seconds is $\left(t^2 - 3t - 2\right)$ m s^{-1}. The displacement of the particle from a fixed point is s metres after t seconds, and $s = 10$ when $t = 6$. Find the formula for s in terms of t.

Use $v = \dfrac{ds}{dt}$ to find an expression for the displacement s.	$v = \dfrac{ds}{dt}$ so $s = \int v\,dt$ $s = \int \left(t^2 - 3t - 2\right)dt$ $= \tfrac{1}{3}t^3 - \tfrac{3}{2}t^2 - 2t + C.$
Use the fact that $s = 10$ when $t = 6$ to find the constant.	When $t = 6$, $s = 10$ so $10 = \tfrac{1}{3} \times 6^3 - \tfrac{3}{2} \times 6^2 - 2 \times 6 + C$ $\qquad = 72 - 54 - 12 + C$ $\qquad = 6 + C$ giving $C = 4$.
Present the result.	Therefore $s = \tfrac{1}{3}t^3 - \tfrac{3}{2}t^2 - 2t + 4.$

2 A particle moves in a straight line with a constant acceleration of 3 m s^{-2}. If its velocity after t seconds is $v \text{ m s}^{-1}$, find v in terms of t, given that the velocity after 2 seconds is 13 m s^{-1}.

Use $a = \dfrac{dv}{dt}$ to find an expression for the velocity v.	$a = \dfrac{dv}{dt}$ so $v = \int a \, dt$ $v = \int 3 \, dt$ $= 3t + C.$
Use the fact that $v = 13$ when $t = 2$ to find the constant.	When $t = 2$, $v = 13$ so $13 = 3 \times 2 + C$ $\qquad = 6 + C$ giving $C = 7$.
Present the result.	Therefore $v = 3t + 7$.

3 A particle moves in a straight line in such a way that its velocity after t seconds is $(2t + 5) \text{ m s}^{-1}$. Find the distance travelled in the first 4 seconds.

Use $v = \dfrac{ds}{dt}$ to find an expression for the displacement s.	$v = \dfrac{ds}{dt}$ so $s = \int v \, dt$ $s = \int (2t + 5) \, dt$ $= t^2 + 5t + C.$
Find expressions for the displacement when $t = 0$ and when $t = 4$.	When $t = 0$, $s = C$. When $t = 4$, $s = 4^2 + 5 \times 4 + C = 36 + C$.
Find the difference between these to find the distance travelled.	The distance travelled is $36 + C - C = 36$ metres.

4 The acceleration a m s^{-2} of a particle moving in a straight line is given by
$a = 6t - 2$. At time $t = 0$ the velocity is 3 m s^{-1} and the displacement is 2 m.
Find the velocity and displacement when $t = 3$.

Use $a = \dfrac{dv}{dt}$ to find an expression for the displacement v.	$a = \dfrac{dv}{dt}$ so $v = \int a \, dt$ $v = \int a \, dt = \int (6t - 2) \, dt$ $\qquad = 3t^2 - 2t + C.$
Use the fact that when $t = 0$, $v = 3$ to find the constant C.	When $t = 0$, $v = 3$ so, substituting in the equation $v = 3t^2 - 2t + C$, $3 = 3 \times 0^2 - 2 \times 0 + C$ or $C = 3$. Therefore $v = 3t^2 - 2t + 3$.
Use $v = \dfrac{ds}{dt}$ to find an expression for the displacement s.	$v = \dfrac{ds}{dt}$ so $s = \int v \, dt$ $s = \int \left(3t^2 - 2t + 3\right) dt$ $\qquad = t^3 - t^2 + 3t + C_1.$
Use the fact that when $t = 0$, $s = 2$ to find the constant C_1.	When $t = 0$, $s = 2$ so, substituting in the equation $s = t^3 - t^2 + 3t + C_1$, $2 = 0^3 - 0^2 + 3 \times 0 + C_1$ or $C_1 = 2$. Therefore $s = t^3 - t^2 + 3t + 2$.
Finally, substititue $t = 3$ into the expressions for velocity and displacement.	When $t = 3$, $v = 3 \times 3^2 - 2 \times 3 + 3 = 24$ and $s = 3^3 - 3^2 + 3 \times 3 + 2 = 29$. Therefore at time 3 seconds the velocity is $v = 24$ m s^{-1} and the displacement is 29 m.

Exercise 4

1   A particle moves in a straight line, and its velocity after t seconds is given by $(36 - 4t)$ m s^{-1}. The displacement of the particle from a fixed point after t seconds is s metres, and $s = 40$ when $t = 1$. Find s in terms of t.

2   A particle is projected from a point A in the line, and its velocity after t seconds is $(48 - 3t)$ cm s^{-1}. If its displacement from A at t seconds is s cm, find s in terms of t. Hence find the time which elapses before the particle is back again at A.

3   A particle moves along a straight line in such a way that its acceleration after t seconds is $(2t + 1)$ cm s^{-2}. If its velocity after t seconds is v cm s^{-1}, find v in terms of t, given that $v = 11$ when $t = 2$.

4   A particle is moving in a straight line in such a way that its velocity after t seconds is $\left(2t^2 - t\right)$ m s^{-1}. Find the distance gone in the first 3 seconds.

5   A body is projected vertically into the air, and its upward velocity after t seconds is $(147 - 9.8t)$ m s^{-1}. If its height after t seconds is h metres, find the formula for h in terms of t. Find also the greatest height reached.

6   A body is moving along a straight line, and its acceleration after t seconds is $(9 - 4t)$ cm s^{-2}. Its velocity after t seconds is v cm s^{-1}, and its initial velocity is 3 cm s^{-1}. Find v in terms of t.

7   A particle moves a long a straight line AB, starting from A, and its velocity after t seconds is $\left(12 - \frac{1}{3}t^2\right)$ m s^{-1}. If s metres is the distance it has gone after t seconds, find s in terms of t. Find also the time that elapses before the particle comes to rest, and its distance from A at that instant.

8   A particle is projected into the air in such a way that its velocity after t seconds is $\left(3t^2 - 4t + 1\right)$ m s^{-1}. The distance of the particle from a fixed point A in the line is s metres after t seconds, and $s = 5$ when $t = 2$. Find the distance of the particle from A (i) initially, (ii) after 1 second, and (iii) after 4 seconds.

9   A body is projected vertically into the air with an initial velocity of 58.8 m s^{-1}, and the constant acceleration due to gravity is 9.8 m s^{-2}. If the velocity after t seconds is v m s^{-1}, find v in terms of t. Find also h in terms of t, where h metres is the height after t seconds. Hence find the height after (i) 5 seconds, (ii) 7 seconds. What do these last two results imply?

5 Calculating area

You will need to know

- the meaning of definite integrals and how to calculate them

- that the area of the region shown shaded in Fig. 5.1 is given by $\int_a^b y\,dx$ or $\int_a^b f(x)\,dx$

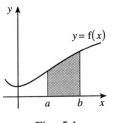

Fig. 5.1

- that the area of the region shown shaded in Fig. 5.2 is given by $\int_a^b x\,dy$ or $\int_a^b f(y)\,dy$

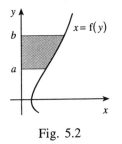

Fig. 5.2

- that if the region corresponding to the integral $\int_a^b y\,dx$ lies below the x-axis, then the integral is negative

- that if the region corresponding to the integral $\int_a^b x\,dy$ lies to the left of the y-axis, then the integral is negative.

Help yourself to integration

1 Find the definite integral $\int_{2}^{5} x^2 \, dx$.

Evaluate the integral, substitute the upper and lower limits and subtract the results.

$$\int_{2}^{5} x^2 \, dx = \left[\tfrac{1}{3}x^3\right]_{2}^{5}$$

$$= \left(\tfrac{1}{3} \times 5^3\right) - \left(\tfrac{1}{3} \times 2^3\right)$$

$$= \tfrac{125}{3} - \tfrac{8}{3} = \tfrac{117}{3} = 39.$$

2 Find the definite integral $\int_{-6}^{-3} \dfrac{1}{x^2} \, dx$.

Evaluate the integral, substitute the upper and lower limits and subtract the results.

$$\int_{-6}^{-3} \frac{1}{x^2} \, dx = \int_{-6}^{-3} x^{-2} \, dx = \left[-x^{-1}\right]_{-6}^{-3}$$

$$= \left[-\frac{1}{x}\right]_{-6}^{-3} = \left(-\tfrac{1}{-3}\right) - \left(-\tfrac{1}{-6}\right) = \tfrac{1}{6}.$$

3 Find the definite integral $\int_{4}^{2} x \, dx$.

Evaluate the integral, substitute the upper and lower limits and subtract the results. This is still correct even though the upper limit is smaller than the lower limit.

$$\int_{4}^{2} x \, dx = \left[\tfrac{1}{2}x^2\right]_{4}^{2}$$

$$= \left(\tfrac{1}{2} \times 2^2\right) - \left(\tfrac{1}{2} \times 4^2\right)$$

$$= 2 - 8 = -6.$$

4 Find the area of the region bounded by the curve $y = 3x^2 - 4x + 2$, the x-axis and the lines $x = 2$ and $x = 5$.

Draw a sketch of the required region, shown in Fig. 5.3. It is important to draw such a sketch diagram, because to use the formula $\int_a^b f(x)\,dx$ the whole region must lie above the *x*-axis, as in Fig. 5.1.

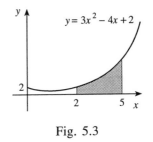

y = 3x² − 4x + 2

Fig. 5.3

Use the formula $\int_a^b f(x)\,dx$ to find the area; the limits are the appropriate values of *x*.

The area $= \int_2^5 \left(3x^2 - 4x + 2\right) dx$

$= \left[x^3 - 2x^2 + 2x\right]_2^5$

$= \left(5^3 - 2 \times 5^2 + 2 \times 5\right)$

$\qquad - \left(2^3 - 2 \times 2^2 + 2 \times 2\right)$

$= 85 - 4 = 81$ units.

You do have to draw a sketch. If part of the area is below the *x*-axis the formula $\int_a^b f(x)\,dx$ does not work in the way you expect.

5 Find the area of the region lying between the curve $y = 18 + 3x - x^2$ and the *x*-axis.

Draw a sketch of the required region, shown in Fig. 5.4.

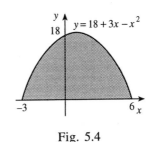

y = 18 + 3x − x²

Fig. 5.4

Find where the graph cuts the *x*-axis by solving the equation $18+3x-x^2=0$.

The graph cuts the *x*-axis where
$18+3x-x^2=0$, that is
$$x^2-3x-18=0$$
$$(x-6)(x+3)=0$$
so $x=-3$ or $x=6$.

Use the formula $\int_a^b f(x)\,dx$ to find the area.

The area $= \int_{-3}^{6}\left(18+3x-x^2\right)dx$

$$=\left[18x+\tfrac{3}{2}x^2-\tfrac{1}{3}x^3\right]_{-3}^{6}$$

$$=\left(18\times6+\tfrac{3}{2}\times6^2-\tfrac{1}{3}\times6^3\right)$$

$$-\left(18\times(-3)+\tfrac{3}{2}\times(-3)^2-\tfrac{1}{3}\times(-3)^3\right)$$

$$=90-\left(-31\tfrac{1}{2}\right)=121\tfrac{1}{2}.$$

6 Find the area of the region lying between the curve $y=x^2$ and the line $y=4x$.

Draw a sketch of the required region, shown in Fig. 5.5.

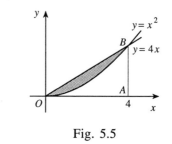

Fig. 5.5

The strategy is to carry out an 'add and subtract' calculation to find the area between the curves. But first you need to find where the curves intersect.

To find where the curves intersect, solve the equations $y=x^2$ and $y=4x$ simultaneously.

$y=x^2$ meets $y=4x$ when
$x^2-4x=0$, that is, $x(x-4)=0$
so $x=0$ and $x=4$.

To find the area under the straight line, you can either use the formula for the area of a triangle, or you can calculate the integral $\int_0^4 4x\,dx$.

Use the formula $\int_0^4 4x\,dx$ to find the area under the line, and $\int_0^4 x^2\,dx$ to find the area under the curve, then subtract.	Area under the line $$= \int_0^4 4x\,dx = \left[2x^2\right]_0^4 = 32.$$ Area under the curve $$= \int_0^4 x^2\,dx = \left[\tfrac{1}{3}x^3\right]_0^4 = \tfrac{64}{3}.$$ Required area $= 32 - \tfrac{64}{3} = \tfrac{32}{3} = 10\tfrac{2}{3}.$

Alternatively, in Example 6 you could find the area of the triangle *OAB* in Fig. 5.5 by using $\tfrac{1}{2} \times$ base $\times$ height and get the area under the line as $\tfrac{1}{2} \times 4 \times 16 = 32$.

7   Find the area of the region lying between the curve $y = x^2 - 6x$ and the *x*-axis.

Draw a sketch of the required region, shown in Fig. 5.6.	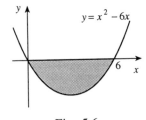

Fig. 5.6

Find where the graph cuts the *x*-axis by solving the equation $x^2 - 6x = 0$.	The graph cuts the *x*-axis where $x^2 - 6x = 0$, that is $x(x-6) = 0$ so $x = 0$ or $x = 6$.

Use the formula $\int_a^b f(x)\,dx$ to find the area.	$\int_0^6 \left(x^2 - 6x\right)dx$ $= \left[\tfrac{1}{3}x^3 - 3x^2\right]_0^6$ $= \left(\tfrac{1}{3} \times 6^3 - 3 \times 6^2\right) - \left(\tfrac{1}{3} \times 0^3 - 3 \times 0^2\right)$ $= -36 - 0 = -36.$

19

Since the area is below the *x*-axis you must expect the result to be negative.

The required area is 36 units.

8 Find the area of the region lying between the curve $y = \sqrt{x}$ and the *y*-axis between $y = 1$ and $y = 4$.

Draw a sketch of the required region, shown in Fig. 5.7.

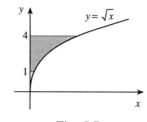

Fig. 5.7

Use the formula $\int_1^4 x\,dy$ to find the area.

Since $y = \sqrt{x}$, $x = y^2$, so required area

$$= \int_1^4 y^2\,dy = \left[\tfrac{1}{3}y^3\right]_1^4$$

$$= \left(\tfrac{1}{3} \times 4^3\right) - \left(\tfrac{1}{3} \times 1^3\right) = 21.$$

Exercise 5

In questions 1 to 14 evaluate the following definite integrals.

1 $\displaystyle\int_1^2 x^2\,dx$

2 $\displaystyle\int_2^4 x^3\,dx$

3 $\displaystyle\int_3^5 2x\,dx$

4 $\displaystyle\int_4^3 3x^2\,dx$

5 $\displaystyle\int_6^4 5x\,dx$

6 $\displaystyle\int_3^8 3\,dx$

7 $\displaystyle\int_0^5 9x^2\,dx$

8 $\displaystyle\int_0^3 8x^3\,dx$

9 $\displaystyle\int_1^2 \frac{5}{x^2}\,dx$

10 $\displaystyle\int_4^2 \frac{4}{x^2}\,dx$

11 $\displaystyle\int_1^6 (6x+2)\,dx$

12 $\displaystyle\int_0^3 (6x^2 - 4x + 1)\,dx$

13 $\displaystyle\int_3^6 \left(x + \frac{1}{x^2} \right) dx$ **14** $\displaystyle\int_4^1 \left(3x^2 - 6x - 4 \right) dx$

In each of the questions 15 to 37, draw a rough sketch of the region involved.

15 Find the area of the region enclosed between the curve $y = x^2$, the x-axis and the lines $x = 1$ and $x = 3$.

16 Find by integration the area of the region bounded by the straight line $y = 2x - 1$, the x-axis and the lines $x = 3$ and $x = 6$.

17 Find the area of the region lying between $y = 3x^2 - 2$ and the x-axis, for values of x from 1 to 3.

18 Find the area of the region lying between $y = 2x^2 - 5x + 6$ and the x-axis, for values of x from 1 to 3.

19 Find the area of the region lying between $y = x^2 - 2x + 1$, the x-axis, and the line $x = 5$.

20 Find the area of the region enclosed by the curve $y = -x^2 + 7x - 10$ and the x-axis.

21 Find the area of the region enclosed by the curve $y = 10 + 3x - x^2$ and the x-axis.

22 Find the area of the region lying between $y = \frac{1}{2}x^2 + 5$ and the x-axis, for values of x from 3 to 4.

23 Find by integration the area of the region bounded by the curve $y = 3x^2 - 12x + 16$, the x-axis, the y-axis and the line $x = 5$.

24 Find the area of the region bounded by the curve $y = 2x + \frac{1}{x^2}$, the x-axis and the lines $x = 2$ and $x = 5$.

25 Find the area of the region lying between the curve $y = -x^2 + 8x - 7$ and the x-axis.

26 Find the area of the region enclosed by the two axes, the line $x = 6$, and the curve $y = x^2 + 4x + 1$.

27 Find the area of the region bounded by the curve $y = 6 + 5x - x^2$ and the x-axis.

28 Find the area of the region lying between the curve $y = x^2$ and the straight line $y = -4x$.

29 Find the area of the region lying between the curves $y = x^2$ and $y = \frac{1}{2}x^2$ from the origin up to the line $x = 6$.

30 Find the area of the region which is bounded by the curve $y = x^2 - 2x + 6$ and the line $y = 3x + 2$.

31 Find the area of the region which is bounded by the curves $y = 2x^2 - x + 4$ and $y = x^2 + x + 7$.

32 Calculate the area of the region between the curve $y = x^2 - 7x + 10$ and the x-axis.

33 Calculate the area of the region between the graph of $y = x^3 - 6x^2 + 11x - 6$, the x-axis and the lines $x = 1$ and $x = 3$. Interpret your answer.

34 Calculate the area of the region between the graph of $y = x^3 - 6x^2 + 11x - 6$, the x-axis and the lines $x = 1$ and $x = 2$.

35 Calculate the total area of the region cut off the graph of $y = x^3 - 6x^2 + 11x - 6$ by the x-axis and the lines $x = 1$ and $x = 3$.

36 Calculate the area of the region between the graph of $y = x^3$, the y-axis and the line $y = 1$.

37 Calculate the area of the region between the graph of $y = x^{\frac{1}{3}}$, the y-axis and the line $y = 1$.

6 Volumes of revolution

You will need to know

- that you obtain a volume of revolution by rotating a curve about an axis

- that the volume of revolution shown in Fig. 6.1 is given by $\pi \int_a^b y^2 \, dx$

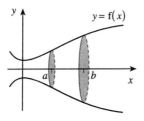

Fig. 6.1

- that the volume of a similar volume of revolution formed by rotating a curve around the y-axis is given by $\pi \int_a^b x^2 \, dy$.

1   The curve $y^2 = 6x$ is rotated about the x-axis. Find the volume generated by that part of the curve which lies between $x = 1$ and $x = 4$.

It is not essential to draw a figure for volumes of revolution, because they always come out as positive numbers.

Use the formula $\pi \int_a^b y^2 \, dx$.	$\text{Volume} = \pi \int_1^4 y^2 \, dx$
Substitute for the value of y from the equation of the curve.	$= \pi \int_1^4 6x \, dx$
	$= \pi \left[3x^2 \right]_1^4$
	$= \pi \left(3 \times 4^2 \right) - \pi \left(3 \times 1^2 \right)$
	$= 48\pi - 3\pi = 45\pi.$

23

Present your result.	The required volume is 45π units.

Note that it is usual to leave the factor π in your results.

2   Find the volume generated by rotating about the *x*-axis that part of the curve $xy = 2$ which lies between the lines $x = 2$ and $x = 8$.

Use the formula $\pi\displaystyle\int_a^b y^2\,dx$.	$\text{Volume} = \pi\displaystyle\int_2^8 y^2\,dx$
Substitute for the value of *y* from the equation of the curve.	$= \pi\displaystyle\int_2^8 \frac{4}{x^2}\,dx = \pi\int_2^8 4x^{-2}\,dx$
	$= \pi\left[-4x^{-1}\right]_2^8 = \pi\left[-\dfrac{4}{x}\right]_2^8$
	$= \pi\left(-\dfrac{4}{8}\right) - \pi\left(-\dfrac{4}{2}\right)$
	$= 2\pi - \tfrac{1}{2}\pi = \tfrac{3}{2}\pi.$
Present your result.	The required volume is $\tfrac{3}{2}\pi$ units.

3   Find the volume generated by rotating about the *y*-axis that part of the curve $y = x^2$ which lies between $x = 0$ and $x = 2$.

Use the formula $\pi\displaystyle\int_a^b x^2\,dy$; the limits are appropriate values of *y*.	$\text{Volume} = \pi\displaystyle\int_0^4 x^2\,dy$

Substitute for the value of x from the equation of the curve.	$$= \pi \int_0^4 y \, dy$$ $$= \pi \left[\tfrac{1}{2} y^2 \right]_0^4$$ $$= \pi \left(\frac{4^2}{2} \right) - \pi(0)$$ $$= 8\pi.$$
Present your result.	The required volume is 8π units.

Exercise 6

In the following questions, do not substitute for π.

1   The curve $y^2 = 5x + 2$ is rotated about the x-axis. Find the volume generated by that part of the curve which lies between $x = 2$ and $x = 4$.

2   Find the volume generated by rotating about the x-axis that part of the curve $y = \tfrac{1}{3} x^2$ which lies between the origin and $x = 3$.

3   Find, by integration, the volume of the cone formed by rotating about the x-axis the line $y = 2x$ for values of x from 0 to 5. Check by calculating the volume of the cone using the usual formula.

4   The curve $y = \dfrac{6}{x}$ is rotated about the x-axis. Find the volume generated for values of x from 2 to 9.

5   The equation $x^2 + y^2 = 9$ represents a circle of radius 3 units, with its centre at the origin. By integrating between $x = -3$ and $x = 3$, find the volume of a sphere of radius 3 units.

6   Find, by integrating, the volume of a frustum of a cone formed by rotating about the x-axis the line $y = \tfrac{1}{3} x$ for values of x from 3 to 6.

7   Find the volume generated by rotating about the x-axis that part of the curve $y = x^2 - x$ which lies between its intersections with the x-axis.

8   The curve $x^2 - y^2 = 4$ is rotated about the x-axis. Find the volume generated by that part of the curve which lies between $x = 3$ and $x = 4$.

9   The equation $x^2 + y^2 = 16$ represents a circle of radius 4 units, with its centre at the origin. Find the volume of a zone of a sphere of radius 4 units, cut off by parallel planes at distances 1 unit and 3 units from the centre.

10 The part of the curve $y = x^2 - x - 2$ between the points where it cuts the x-axis is rotated about that axis. Find the volume so generated.

11 A wooden cylinder has a radius of 4 units and height 2 units. Its axis lies along the positive x-axis, and one end of the axis is at the origin. A lathe cuts out of this cylinder a shape equivalent to the volume of revolution formed by the curve $y = x^2$ between $x = 0$ and $x = 2$. Find the volume of wood remaining.

12 The part of the curve $y = \sqrt{x}$ between $y = 1$ and $y = 4$ is rotated about the y-axis. Find the volume of the solid of revolution formed.

13 The region between the curves $y = \sqrt{x}$ and $y = x^2$ is rotated about the x-axis. Find the volume of the solid of revolution formed.

14 The region between the curve $y = \sqrt{x}$ and the line $y = x$ is rotated about the y-axis. Find the volume of the solid of revolution formed.

7 Using standard forms to integrate

You will need to know

- $\int x^n \, dx = \dfrac{1}{n+1} x^{n+1} + C$, provided $n \neq -1$

- $\int \dfrac{1}{x} \, dx = \ln x + C$ if $x > 0$ and $\int \dfrac{1}{x} \, dx = \ln(-x) + C$ if $x < 0$, that is $\int \dfrac{1}{x} \, dx = \ln|x| + C$

- $\int e^x \, dx = e^x + C$ and $\int e^{ax} \, dx = \dfrac{1}{a} e^{ax} + C$

- $\int \sin x \, dx = -\cos x + C$ and $\int \sin ax \, dx = -\dfrac{1}{a} \cos ax + C$

- $\int \cos x \, dx = \sin x + C$ and $\int \cos ax \, dx = \dfrac{1}{a} \sin ax + C$

- the composite function rule (chain rule) for differentiation, and how to use it in reverse.

1 Integrate $2x^4$.

Use $\int x^n \, dx = \dfrac{1}{n+1} x^{n+1} + C$.

$$\int 2x^4 \, dx = 2 \int x^4 \, dx$$
$$= 2 \times \tfrac{1}{5} x^5 + C = \tfrac{2}{5} x^5 + C.$$

You may be able to leave out some of the steps. But whatever you do, you should always check your answer by differentiation, and never leave out the constant of integration.

2 Find $\int \dfrac{2}{x} \, dx$.

Use $\int \dfrac{1}{x} \, dx = \ln|x| + C$.

$$\int \dfrac{2}{x} \, dx = 2 \int \dfrac{1}{x} \, dx$$
$$= 2 \ln|x| + C.$$

Help yourself to integration

You should remember what $\ln|x|$ means. If $x = 5$, then $\ln|x| = \ln|5| = \ln 5$; but if $x = -7$, then $\ln|x| = \ln|-7| = \ln 7$.

3 Find $\int 3\cos 4x\,dx$.

Use $\int \cos ax\,dx = \dfrac{1}{a}\sin ax + C$.

$$\int 3\cos 4x\,dx = 3\int \cos 4x\,dx$$
$$= 3 \times \frac{1}{4}\sin 4x + C$$
$$= \tfrac{3}{4}\sin x + C.$$

It is at this point that you first see the essence of this chapter, which is to use the composite function rule in reverse. Suppose that you are calculating $\int e^{2x}\,dx$. The key is to recognise that when you differentiate e^{2x} you get e^{2x} multiplied by the derivative of $2x$, that is, 2. So a first guess at the integral $\int e^{2x}\,dx$ is e^{2x}; you can then check the multiplying constant by differentiation.

4 Find $\int e^{2x}\,dx$.

Notice that the derivative of e^{2x} is a multiple of e^{2x}; this shows that the integral is a constant $\times e^{2x}$.

To find $\int e^{2x}\,dx$, try e^{2x}.

Then $\dfrac{d}{dx}\left(e^{2x}\right) = 2e^{2x}$.

Make the adjustment for the multiplying factor.

Therefore $\int e^{2x}\,dx = \tfrac{1}{2}e^{2x} + C$.

Integration is harder than differentiation. However, you can always check your answer to an integration problem by differentiating your proposed integral. This is rather like checking a solution of an equation; you should always do it, even if you only do it mentally.

This process will be called 'guess and check'. First you guess the essential part of the integral. Then you check the multiplying constant by differentiation.

5   Find the integral of $(2x+1)^4$.

Notice that the derivative of $(2x+1)^5$ is a multiple of $(2x+1)^4$; as a first guess, try as the integral $(2x+1)^5$.	Try as the first guess $(2x+1)^5$. Then $$\frac{d}{dx}\left((2x+1)^5\right)=5\times(2x+1)^4\times 2.$$
Make the adjustment for the multiplying factor. In this case the multiple is $5\times 2=10$.	Thus $\int(2x+1)^4\,dx=\tfrac{1}{10}(2x+1)^5+C$.

6   Evaluate $\int x\cos\left(x^2\right)dx$.

In this case, you might try as a first guess $\cos\left(x^2\right)$, since a multiple of the derivative of $\left(x^2\right)$, namely x is outside the term $\cos\left(x^2\right)$.	Try as the first guess $\cos\left(x^2\right)$. Then $\dfrac{d}{dx}\left(\cos\left(x^2\right)\right)=-\sin\left(x^2\right)\times 2x$.

This shows that the first guess was wrong. But it should also show you that a better try would have been $\sin\left(x^2\right)$.

Try $\sin\left(x^2\right)$ instead.	Then $\dfrac{d}{dx}\left(\sin\left(x^2\right)\right)=\cos\left(x^2\right)\times 2x$.
Since $\cos\left(x^2\right)\times 2x=2x\cos\left(x^2\right)$ it is a constant multiple of $x\cos\left(x^2\right)$.	Thus $\int x\cos\left(x^2\right)dx=\tfrac{1}{2}\sin\left(x^2\right)+C$.

Help yourself to integration

7 Find $\int \dfrac{x}{1+x^2}\,dx$.

This looks tricky, and you need to remember that $\dfrac{d}{dx}\big(\ln(f(x))\big) = \dfrac{f'(x)}{f(x)}$.

Try as the first guess $\ln\left(1+x^2\right)$.

Then $\dfrac{d}{dx}\left(\ln\left(1+x^2\right)\right) = \dfrac{1}{1+x^2} \times 2x$.

Since $\dfrac{1}{1+x^2} \times 2x = \dfrac{2x}{1+x^2}$, it is a constant multiple of $\dfrac{x}{1+x^2}$.

Thus $\int \dfrac{x}{1+x^2}\,dx = \tfrac{1}{2}\ln\left(1+x^2\right) + C$.

This form is so important that it is worth remembering as a special case for use when you need it. If you see the form $\int \dfrac{f'(x)}{f(x)}\,dx$ where the numerator is a multiple of the derivative of the denominator, then the integral will be a natural logarithm.

Sometimes there may be alternative forms for the answer, and they may occasionally look quite different from your form. For example, using the laws of logarithms, $\tfrac{1}{2}\ln\left(1+x^2\right) = \ln\left(1+x^2\right)^{\frac{1}{2}} = \ln\sqrt{1+x^2}$, so an alternative, rather different looking, answer may be $\ln\sqrt{1+x^2} + C$.

Or you could write instead of C, $\ln C$, which would still be a constant. Then the result would be $\ln\sqrt{1+x^2} + \ln C$, which you can write, using the laws of logarithms again, as $\ln C\sqrt{1+x^2}$.

The important thing is that all three forms are correct as integrals of $\dfrac{x}{1+x^2}$, as you can check by differentiation. The moral is not to be put off by a different form for an answer.

8 Find $\int x^2\left(x^3+1\right)^2\,dx$.

One way to approach this is to multiply out the bracket, but it is better to notice that x^2 is a multiple of the derivative of $\left(x^3+1\right)$.

Try as the first guess $\left(x^3+1\right)^3$.

Then $\dfrac{d}{dx}\left(x^3+1\right)^3 = 3\left(x^3+1\right)^2 \times 3x^2$

$$= 9x^2\left(x^3+1\right)^2.$$

The constant multiple is 9.

So

$$\int x^2\left(x^3+1\right)^2 dx = \tfrac{1}{9}x^2\left(x^3+1\right)^2 + C.$$

9 Find the integral of $\dfrac{x}{\sqrt{2+x^2}}$.

Re-write this in an index form. Remember that you can't integrate or differentiate results involving square roots unless you put them into index form.

$$\int \frac{x}{\sqrt{2+x^2}}\,dx = \int x\left(2+x^2\right)^{-\frac{1}{2}}\,dx.$$

You may now see the pattern, that $\left(2+x^2\right)^{\frac{1}{2}}$ is a good first guess, because the bracket $\left(2+x^2\right)^{-\frac{1}{2}}$ is multiplied by a multiple of the derivative of $\left(2+x^2\right)$.

Then $\dfrac{d}{dx}\left(2+x^2\right)^{\frac{1}{2}} = \tfrac{1}{2}\left(2+x^2\right)^{-\frac{1}{2}} \times 2x$

$$= x\left(2+x^2\right)^{-\frac{1}{2}}.$$

Thus $\displaystyle\int \frac{x}{\sqrt{2+x^2}}\,dx = \left(2+x^2\right)^{\frac{1}{2}} + C.$

In fact, in Example 9 the power of $\left(2+x^2\right)$ has been raised by one. This also occurs in Example 10.

10 Calculate $\int \dfrac{dx}{\sqrt{x+2}}$.

Re-write this in an index form.	$\int \dfrac{dx}{\sqrt{x+2}} = \int (x+2)^{-\frac{1}{2}} \, dx$.
This is a power, so raise the power by 1 to get to your first guess, $(x+2)^{\frac{1}{2}}$.	Then $\dfrac{d}{dx}(x+2)^{\frac{1}{2}} = \frac{1}{2}(x+2)^{-\frac{1}{2}} \times 1$ $= \frac{1}{2}(x+2)^{-\frac{1}{2}}$.
The constant multiple is $\frac{1}{2}$, so divide by it, that is, multiply by 2.	$\int \dfrac{dx}{\sqrt{x+2}} = 2(x+2)^{\frac{1}{2}} + C$.

11 Calculate $\int \sqrt{2x} \, dx$.

Re-write this in an index form.	$\int \sqrt{2x} \, dx = \int (2x)^{\frac{1}{2}} \, dx$.
Take the factor of $2^{\frac{1}{2}}$ out of the bracket.	$\int (2x)^{\frac{1}{2}} \, dx = 2^{\frac{1}{2}} \int x^{\frac{1}{2}} \, dx$.
Now you can integrate using the standard methods.	$2^{\frac{1}{2}} \int x^{\frac{1}{2}} \, dx = 2^{\frac{1}{2}} \times \frac{2}{3} x^{\frac{3}{2}} + C$ $= \dfrac{2\sqrt{2}}{3} x^{\frac{3}{2}} + C$.

12 Calculate $\int \sin^3 x \cos x \, dx$.

You can think of $\int \sin^3 x \cos x \, dx$ as $\int (\sin x)^3 \cos x \, dx$.	$\int (\sin x)^3 \cos x \, dx = \frac{1}{4} \sin^4 x + C$.

Exercise 7

Find the following integrals using the guess and check technique.

1 $\int 3x^4\, dx$

2 $\int 2x^5\, dx$

3 $\int 4x^{-\frac{1}{2}}\, dx$

4 $\int \dfrac{2}{x^2}\, dx$

5 $\int x^2\left(1+x^2\right) dx$

6 $\int \dfrac{x^2+1}{x}\, dx$

7 $\int \sqrt{x}\left(1+\sqrt{x}\right) dx$

8 $\int \dfrac{x+1}{x^2}\, dx$

9 $\int (2x-5)(2x+5)\, dx$

10 $\int \dfrac{(x+1)^2}{x}\, dx$

11 $\int \dfrac{2}{x}\, dx$

12 $\int \dfrac{1}{2x}\, dx$

13 $\int -\dfrac{1}{x}\, dx$

14 $\int -2x^{-1}\, dx$

15 $\int \sin x\, dx$

16 $\int -\cos x\, dx$

17 $\int 2e^{3x}\, dx$

18 $\int 4e^{2x}\, dx$

19 $\int 3e^{-2x}\, dx$

20 $\int 2e^{-2x}\, dx$

21 $\int e^{-x}\, dx$

22 $\int e^{ax+b}\, dx$

23 $\int e^{\frac{1}{3}x}\, dx$

24 $\int -2e^{-\frac{1}{2}x}\, dx$

25 $\int \left(e^{\frac{1}{2}x}+e^{-\frac{1}{2}x}\right)^2 dx$

26 $\int \left(e^{\frac{1}{2}x}-e^{-\frac{1}{2}x}\right)^2 dx$

27 $\int (3x+2)^5\, dx$

28 $\int (x+2)^3\, dx$

29 $\int (1-x)^6\, dx$

30 $\int (5-3x)^2\, dx$

31 $\int (1+2x)^{-2}\, dx$

32 $\int 3(1-2x)^{-4}\, dx$

33 $\int 2\left(1+\tfrac{1}{3}x\right)^{\frac{1}{2}} dx$

34 $\int 2\left(1+\tfrac{1}{4}x\right)^{-\frac{1}{2}} dx$

35 $\int \cos 2x\, dx$

36 $\int 4\sin 4x\, dx$

37 $\int 2\sin(-2x)\, dx$

38 $\int \cos\left(\tfrac{1}{2}\pi x\right) dx$

39 $\int x\sin(x^2)\,dx$

40 $\int \sin(\pi x)\,dx$

41 $\int \sin(ax+b)\,dx$

42 $\int \cos\omega(x-\tfrac{1}{4}\pi)\,dx$

43 $\int \dfrac{2}{1+x}\,dx$

44 $\int \dfrac{3}{2+3x}\,dx$

45 $\int \dfrac{-1}{1-x}\,dx$

46 $\int \dfrac{1}{x-1}\,dx$

47 $\int \dfrac{1}{2(1+3x)}\,dx$

48 $\int \dfrac{5}{(4-5x)}\,dx$

49 $\int \dfrac{1}{1-7x}\,dx$

50 $\int \dfrac{9}{2-3x}\,dx$

51 $\int \dfrac{2x}{1-x^2}\,dx$

52 $\int \dfrac{x^2}{x^3-1}\,dx$

53 $\int \dfrac{\cos x}{\sin x}\,dx$

54 $\int \dfrac{\sin x}{\cos x}\,dx$

55 $\int \dfrac{x}{\sqrt{1-x^2}}\,dx$

56 $\int x(1-x^2)^n\,dx \quad (n\neq -1)$

57 $\int \dfrac{2}{\sqrt{1+2x}}\,dx$

58 $\int \dfrac{4x}{\sqrt{3+2x^2}}\,dx$

59 $\int \dfrac{\cos x}{\sqrt{\sin x}}\,dx$

60 $\int \dfrac{e^x}{\sqrt{1+e^x}}\,dx$

61 $\int \dfrac{x^3}{\sqrt{1-x^4}}\,dx$

62 $\dfrac{2x(1+x^2)}{\sqrt{2x^2+x^4}}$

63 $\int \sqrt{3x}\,dx$

64 $\int \dfrac{1}{\sqrt{2x}}\,dx$

65 $\int (3x)^{\frac{1}{3}}\,dx$

66 $\int \dfrac{1}{2x}\,dx$

67 $\int \dfrac{\sin x}{(2+\cos x)^2}\,dx$

68 $\int (1+2\sin x)^3 \cos x\,dx$

69 $\int \dfrac{\cos x}{(3+2\sin x)}\,dx$

70 $\int \dfrac{e^x}{\sqrt{1+e^x}}\,dx$

8 Some special integrals

Some integrals are awkward and it is not obvious how to tackle them. You need special methods for them.

You will need to know that

- the trigonometric formulae for $\cos 2x$ in the forms $2\sin^2 x = 1 - \cos 2x$ and $2\cos^2 x = 1 + \cos 2x$

- how to use partial fractions.

1   Integrating $\sin^2 x$ and $\cos^2 x$.

To integrate $\sin^2 x$ and $\cos^2 x$ you need the trigonometric formulae
$2\sin^2 x = 1 - \cos 2x$ and
$2\cos^2 x = 1 + \cos 2x$.

$$\int \sin^2 x \, dx = \tfrac{1}{2}\int 2\sin^2 x \, dx$$
$$= \tfrac{1}{2}\int (1 - \cos 2x) \, dx.$$

Now it is in a form that you can integrate.

$$\int \sin^2 x \, dx = \tfrac{1}{2}\left(x - \tfrac{1}{2}\sin 2x\right) + C.$$

In some ways this is no different from a number of the integrals you have seen before. You need to transform the integral into a form that you can integrate.

Here is another example which appears in a different form in Exercise 7, number 52.

2   Find $\displaystyle\int \tan x \, dx$.

Write $\tan x = \dfrac{\sin x}{\cos x}$ and then use the fact that the numerator is the derivative of the denominator.

$$\int \tan x \, dx = \int \frac{\sin x}{\cos x} \, dx$$
$$= -\ln|\cos x| + C.$$

It is difficult to give rules for this kind of transformation. You have to try ideas which seem promising.

3 Find $\int \tan^2 x \, dx$.

Use the identity $1 + \tan^2 x = \sec^2 x$ to transform the integral.

$\int \tan^2 x \, dx = \int \left(\sec^2 x - 1 \right) dx$

$= \tan x - x + C.$

Sometimes you can use trigonometric formulae to help you to integrate.

4 Find $\int \sin 4x \cos 3x \, dx$.

Use the identity
$2 \sin A \cos B = \sin(A + B) + \sin(A - B)$
to transform the integral.

$\int \sin 4x \cos 3x \, dx$

$= \frac{1}{2} \int 2 \sin 4x \cos 3x \, dx$

$= \frac{1}{2} \int \left(\sin 7x + \sin x \right) dx$

$= -\frac{1}{14} \cos 7x - \frac{1}{2} \cos x + C.$

Here is another kind of integral where you have first to transform the integrand.

5 Integrate $\dfrac{2}{(x+1)(x+3)}$.

To integrate $\dfrac{2}{(x+1)(x+3)}$, you need to split it into its individual components

by using partial fractions. That is, if you know $\dfrac{2}{(x+1)(x+3)} = \dfrac{1}{x+1} - \dfrac{1}{x+3}$,

you ought to be able to carry out the integration.

Split $\dfrac{2}{(x+1)(x+3)}$ into its partial fractions.

$\dfrac{2}{(x+1)(x+3)} = \dfrac{A}{x+1} + \dfrac{B}{x+3}$

Multiply both sides by $(x+1)(x+3)$.	$2 = A(x+3) + B(x+1)$.
Equate coefficients of x and the constant term.	$A + B = 0$ $3A + B = 2$.
Solve the equation simultaneously.	$A = 1, B = -1$.
Integrate.	$\int \dfrac{2}{(x+1)(x+3)}\,dx$ $= \int \left(\dfrac{1}{x+1} - \dfrac{1}{x+3} \right) dx$ $= \ln\lvert x+1 \rvert - \ln\lvert x+3 \rvert + C$.

You could also write the previous answer in the very different looking form
$\int \dfrac{2}{(x+1)(x+3)}\,dx = \ln\left\lvert \dfrac{A(x+1)}{x+3} \right\rvert$ by taking the constant to be $\ln A$ instead of C, and by using the properties of logarithms to simplify your result.

6 Find $\displaystyle\int \dfrac{8-7x}{(3x-2)(x+1)}\,dx$.

Split $\dfrac{8-7x}{(3x-2)(x+1)}$ into its partial fractions.	Let $\dfrac{8-7x}{(3x-2)(x+1)} = \dfrac{A}{3x-2} + \dfrac{B}{x+1}$.
Multiply both sides by $(3x-2)(x+1)$.	$8-7x = A(x+1) + B(3x-2)$.
Equate coefficients of x and the constant term.	$A + 3B = -7$ $A - 2B = 8$.
Solve the equation simultaneously.	$A = 2, B = -3$.

Help yourself to integration

Integrate.

$$\int \frac{8-7x}{(3x-2)(x+1)}\,dx$$

$$= \int \left(\frac{2}{3x-2} - \frac{3}{x+1} \right) dx$$

$$= \tfrac{2}{3}\ln|3x-2| - 3\ln|x+1| + C.$$

7 Find $\displaystyle\int \frac{2x+3}{(x+1)^2}\,dx$.

You can integrate $\dfrac{2x+3}{(x+1)^2}$ *if it is in the form* $\dfrac{A}{x+1} + \dfrac{B}{(x+1)^2}$.

Split $\dfrac{2x+3}{(x+1)^2}$ into its partial fractions.

Let $\dfrac{2x+3}{(x+1)^2} = \dfrac{A}{x+1} + \dfrac{B}{(x+1)^2}$.

Multiply both sides by $(x+1)^2$.

$2x+3 = A(x+1) + B.$

Equate coefficients of x and the constant term.

$A = 2$
$A + B = 3.$

Solve the equation simultaneously.

$A = 2,\ B = 1.$

Integrate.

$$\int \frac{2}{(x+1)(x+3)}\,dx$$

$$= \int \left(\frac{2}{x+1} + \frac{1}{(x+1)^2} \right) dx$$

$$= 2\ln|x+1| - \frac{1}{x+1} + C.$$

Sometimes the expression in the numerator has an equal or higher power than the expression in the denominator. If that is the case, you need to divide first.

8   Find $\displaystyle\int \frac{x^2 - x - 10}{x^2 - 4} \, dx$.

Divide and split into partial fractions.	Let $\dfrac{x^2 - x - 10}{x^2 - 4}$ $\qquad = A + \dfrac{B}{x+2} + \dfrac{C}{x-2}.$
Multiply both sides by $x^2 - 4$.	$x^2 - x - 10$ $\qquad = A(x^2 - 4) + B(x-2) + C(x+2).$
Equate coefficients of powers of x and the constant term.	$A \qquad\qquad = 1$ $\qquad B + C = -1$ $-4A - 2B + 2C = -10.$
Solve the equation simultaneously.	$A = 1,\ B = 1,\ C = -2.$
Integrate.	$\displaystyle\int \frac{x^2 - x - 10}{x^2 - 4} \, dx$ $\displaystyle = \int \left(1 + \frac{1}{x+2} - \frac{2}{x-2}\right) dx$ $= x + \ln|x+2| - 2\ln|x-2| + C.$

Exercise 8

Find the following integrals.

1 $\displaystyle\int \cos^2 x \, dx$

2 $\displaystyle\int \sin^2 \tfrac{1}{2} x \, dx$

3 $\displaystyle\int \frac{1}{\cos^2 x} \, dx$

4 $\displaystyle\int \cot^2 x \, dx$

5 $\displaystyle\int \cot x \, dx$

6 $\displaystyle\int \cos^2 2x \, dx$

7 $\displaystyle\int \frac{1}{\sin^2 x} \, dx$

8 $\displaystyle\int \sin^4 x \, dx$

9 $\displaystyle\int \sqrt{1 + \cos 2x} \, dx$

10 $\displaystyle\int \sin x \cos x \, dx$

Help yourself to integration

11 $\displaystyle\int 2\sin 2x\cos x\,dx$

12 $\displaystyle\int \cos 2x\cos 4x\,dx$

13 $\displaystyle\int \sin 3x\sin x\,dx$

14 $\displaystyle\int 2\sin 2x\cos 4x\,dx$

15 $\displaystyle\int \frac{3x+1}{(x-1)(x+1)}\,dx$

16 $\displaystyle\int \frac{5x}{(x-3)(x+2)}\,dx$

17 $\displaystyle\int \frac{10}{(4x-3)(2x+1)}\,dx$

18 $\displaystyle\int \frac{12x+1}{6x^2+x-1}\,dx$

19 $\displaystyle\int \frac{2x+5}{(x+1)^2}\,dx$

20 $\displaystyle\int \frac{4x-1}{(2x-1)^2}\,dx$

21 $\displaystyle\int \frac{6x-13}{(2x-5)^2}\,dx$

22 $\displaystyle\int \frac{x}{(x+2)^2}\,dx$

23 $\displaystyle\int \frac{x^2+x-1}{(x-1)(x+1)}\,dx$

24 $\displaystyle\int \frac{x^2}{x^2-4}\,dx$

25 $\displaystyle\int \frac{x^2+1}{(x+1)^2}\,dx$

26 $\displaystyle\int \frac{x^2}{(x-2)(x+3)}\,dx$

9 Integration by substitution

You will need to know

- the composite function rule for differentiation
- how to make a substitution in an integral
- the inverse trigonometric functions, and their domains of definition.

The idea of integration by substitution is to change the variable in an integral, and, with luck, to transform the integral into a standard form which you recognise.

1   Find the integral $\displaystyle\int \frac{x}{\sqrt{2x-3}}\,dx$.

You cannot transform this using the methods of previous chapters. In this situation it is worth try a substitution for the 'awkward' part of the expression. In this case try substituting $z = 2x - 3$.

When you make a substitution in an integral, you need also to substitute for dx. So you need to differentiate the equation $z = 2x - 3$.	Let $z = 2x - 3$. Then $dz = 2dx$.
Express x in terms of z and make the substitution. You can now integrate the expression in z.	$\displaystyle\int \frac{x}{\sqrt{2x-3}}\,dx = \int \frac{\frac{1}{2}(z+3)}{\sqrt{z}} \times \tfrac{1}{2}\,dz$.
Integrate the expression in z.	$\displaystyle\int \frac{\frac{1}{2}(z+3)}{\sqrt{z}} \times \tfrac{1}{2}\,dz = \int \left(\tfrac{1}{4}z^{\frac{1}{2}} + \tfrac{3}{4}z^{-\frac{1}{2}}\right)dz$ $\qquad\qquad = \tfrac{1}{6}z^{\frac{3}{2}} + \tfrac{3}{2}z^{\frac{1}{2}} + C.$
Substitute back so that the result is given in terms of x.	$\displaystyle\int \frac{x}{\sqrt{2x-3}}\,dx$ $\qquad = \tfrac{1}{6}(2x-3)^{\frac{3}{2}} + \tfrac{3}{2}(2x-3)^{\frac{1}{2}} + C.$

You could also integrate $\int \frac{x}{\sqrt{2x-3}}\,dx$ by making the substitution $z=\sqrt{2x-3}$. This substitution is made in Example 2.

2 Find the integral $\int \frac{x}{\sqrt{2x-3}}\,dx$ by making the substitution $z=\sqrt{2x-3}$.

Differentiate $z=\sqrt{2x-3}$ to make the substitution for dx.	Let $z=\sqrt{2x-3}=(2x-3)^{\frac{1}{2}}$. Then $dz=2\times\frac{1}{2}(2x-3)^{-\frac{1}{2}}\,dx$ $=\frac{1}{\sqrt{2x-3}}\,dx$.
Express x in terms of z to get $x=\frac{1}{2}\left(z^2+3\right)$, make the substitution and integrate. It is good practice first to substitute for the dx.	$\int \frac{x}{\sqrt{2x-3}}\,dx=\int\left(x\times\frac{dx}{\sqrt{2x-3}}\right)$ $=\int \frac{1}{2}\left(z^2+3\right)dz$ $=\frac{1}{6}z^3+\frac{3}{2}z+C.$
Substitute back so that the result is given in terms of x.	$\int \frac{x}{\sqrt{2x-3}}\,dx$ $=\frac{1}{6}(2x-3)^{\frac{3}{2}}+\frac{3}{2}(2x-3)^{\frac{1}{2}}+C.$

In Example 2, the substitution is more difficult, but the integration is easier. Unfortunately, you don't usually win both ways!

3 Find $\int \frac{x^3}{x^2+2}\,dx$.

Substitute for the part of the integrand which appears awkward.	Let $z=x^2+2$.
Differentiate $z=x^2+2$ to make the substitution for dx.	Then $dz=2x\,dx$.

<table>
<tr><td>

Make the substitution, substituting first for dx. Then integrate.

</td><td>

$$\int \frac{x^3}{x^2+2}\,dx = \int \left(\frac{1}{2} \times \frac{x^2}{x^2+2} \times 2x \right) dx$$

$$= \int \left(\frac{1}{2} \times \frac{z-2}{z} \right) \times dz$$

$$= \int \left(\frac{1}{2} - \frac{1}{z} \right) dz$$

$$= \tfrac{1}{2} z - \ln|z| + C.$$

</td></tr>
<tr><td>

Substitute back so that the result is given in terms of x.

</td><td>

$$\int \frac{x^3}{x^2+2}\,dx$$

$$= \tfrac{1}{2}\left(x^2+2\right) - \ln\left(x^2+2\right) + C.$$

</td></tr>
</table>

Note that there is no need for the modulus sign in the logarithmic term because $\left(x^2+2\right)$ is always positive.

Here is an example where the 'obvious' substitution does not work.

4 Find $\displaystyle\int \frac{1}{\sqrt{4-x^2}}\,dx$.

<table>
<tr><td>

Substitute for the part of the integrand which appears awkward.

</td><td>

Let $z = 4 - x^2$.

</td></tr>
<tr><td>

Differentiate $z = 4 - x^2$ to make the substitution for dx.

</td><td>

Then $dz = -2x\,dx$.

</td></tr>
<tr><td>

Make the substitution, substituting first for dx.

</td><td>

$$\int \frac{1}{\sqrt{4-x^2}}\,dx = \int \frac{1}{2x\sqrt{4-x^2}} \times -2x\,dx$$

$$= \int \frac{1}{2\sqrt{4-z}\sqrt{z}} \times dz$$

$$= \int \frac{1}{2\sqrt{4z-z^2}}\,dz.$$

</td></tr>
</table>

The final integral is no easier than the original. The method of integration by substitution is not infallible. There must be a better way!

However, there is a trigonometric substitution which works.

5 Find $\displaystyle\int \frac{1}{\sqrt{4-x^2}}\,dx$.

Try the substitution $x = 2\sin\theta$.	Let $x = 2\sin\theta$.
Differentiate $x = 2\sin\theta$ to make the substitution for dx.	Then $dx = 2\cos\theta\,d\theta$.
Make the substitution, substituting first for dx, and integrate.	$\displaystyle\int \frac{1}{\sqrt{4-x^2}}\,dx = \int \frac{2\cos\theta\,d\theta}{\sqrt{4-4\sin^2\theta}}$ $\displaystyle = \int \frac{2\cos\theta\,d\theta}{\sqrt{4\cos^2\theta}}$ $\displaystyle = \int d\theta = \theta + C.$
Substitute back so that the result is given in terms of x.	$\displaystyle\int \frac{1}{\sqrt{4-x^2}}\,dx = \sin^{-1}\!\left(\tfrac{1}{2}x\right) + C.$

The reason that this substitution has worked so well is that you can take the square root of $4 - 4\sin^2\theta$.

Here is another trigonometric example.

6 Find $\displaystyle\int \frac{1}{9+x^2}\,dx$.

Try the substitution $x = 3\tan\theta$.	Let $x = 3\tan\theta$.
Differentiate $x = 3\tan\theta$ to make the substitution for dx.	Then $dx = 3\sec^2\theta\,d\theta$.

Make the substitution, substituting first for dx, and integrate.	$\displaystyle\int \frac{1}{9+x^2}\,dx = \int \frac{3\sec^2\theta\,d\theta}{9+9\tan^2\theta}$
	$\displaystyle = \int \frac{3\sec^2\theta\,d\theta}{9\sec^2\theta}$
	$\displaystyle = \int \tfrac{1}{3}\,d\theta = \tfrac{1}{3}\theta + C.$
Substitute back so that the result is given in terms of x.	$\displaystyle\int \frac{1}{9+x^2}\,dx = \tfrac{1}{3}\tan^{-1}\left(\tfrac{1}{3}x\right) + C.$

When the integral is a definite integral, you can either proceed as in the examples above, or you can change the limits to fit the new variable in the integral.

7 Find $\displaystyle\int_0^1 x\sqrt{1-x}\,dx$.

Try the substitution $y = 1 - x$.	Let $y = 1 - x$.
Differentiate $y = 1 - x$ to make the substitution for dx.	Then $dy = -dx$.
Make the substitution, substituting first for dx.	$\displaystyle\int_0^1 x\sqrt{1-x}\,dx = \int_{x=0}^{x=1} (1-y)\sqrt{y}\times -dy.$

Notice how, for the moment, the limits have been written from $x = 0$ to $x = 1$ to make it clear that these are x limits and not y limits.

Now use the equation $y = 1 - x$ to change the limits.	When $x = 0$, $y = 1$, so the new lower limit is 1. When $x = 1$, $y = 0$, so the new upper limit is 0. So $\displaystyle\int_0^1 x\sqrt{1-x}\,dx = \int_1^0 (1-y)\sqrt{y}\times -dy.$

Integrate.

$$\int_0^1 x\sqrt{1-x}\,dx = \int_1^0 (1-y)\sqrt{y} \times -dy$$

$$= -\int_1^0 \left(y^{\frac{1}{2}} - y^{\frac{3}{2}}\right)dy$$

$$= -\left[\tfrac{2}{3}y^{\frac{3}{2}} - \tfrac{2}{5}y^{\frac{5}{2}}\right]_1^0$$

$$= -\left\{(0) - \left(\tfrac{2}{3} - \tfrac{2}{5}\right)\right\}$$

$$= \tfrac{4}{15}.$$

8 Integrate $\displaystyle\int_1^4 \frac{1}{\sqrt{x}+4}\,dx$.

Try the substitution $y = \sqrt{x}+4$.

Let $y = \sqrt{x}+4$.

Differentiate $y = \sqrt{x}+4$ to make the substitution for dx.

Then $dy = \tfrac{1}{2}x^{-\frac{1}{2}}\,dx = \dfrac{1}{2(y-4)}\,dx$

so $2(y-4)dy = dx$.

Make the substitution, substituting first for dx.

$$\int_1^4 \frac{1}{\sqrt{x}+4}\,dx = \int_{x=1}^{x=4} \frac{2(y-4)\,dy}{y}.$$

Now use the equation $y = \sqrt{x}+4$ to change the limits.

When $x = 1$, $y = 5$, so the new lower limit is 5.
When $x = 4$, $y = 6$, so the new upper limit is 6.

So $\displaystyle\int_1^4 \frac{1}{\sqrt{x}+4}\,dx = \int_5^6 \frac{2(y-4)\,dy}{y}$.

Integrate.

$$\int_1^4 \frac{1}{\sqrt{x}+4}\,dx = \int_5^6 \frac{2(y-4)\,dy}{y}$$

$$= \int_5^6 \left(2-\frac{8}{y}\right)dy$$

$$= \left[2y-8\ln|y|\right]_5^6$$

$$= (12-8\ln6)-(10-8\ln5)$$

$$= 2-8\ln\tfrac{6}{5}.$$

Exercise 9

In questions 1 to 12, use the given substitution to evaluate the given integral. In some of them, you may be able to integrate by inspection, using the methods of Chapter 7. Nevertheless, use the substitution for the practice.

1	$\int x\sqrt{x-3}\,dx$	$z=x-3$
2	$\int (x+2)\sqrt{x-2}\,dx$	$z=x-2$
3	$\int x\sqrt{2x+1}\,dx$	$z=2x+1$
4	$\int (2x-1)\sqrt{2x-3}\,dx$	$z=2x-3$
5	$\int x\sqrt{3x-2}\,dx$	$z=\sqrt{3x-2}$
6	$\int x^2\sqrt{2x+1}\,dx$	$z=\sqrt{2x+1}$
7	$\int \dfrac{dx}{\sqrt{1+2x}}$	$z=1+2x$
8	$\int \dfrac{x^3\,dx}{\sqrt{1+x^2}}$	$z=1+x^2$
9	$\int \dfrac{x\,dx}{\sqrt{9-x^2}}$	$z=9-x^2$
10	$\int \dfrac{dx}{\sqrt{9-x^2}}$	$x=3\sin\theta$
11	$\int \dfrac{x^3\,dx}{4+x^2}$	$z=4+x^2$

1 2 $\displaystyle\int \frac{dx}{4+x^2}$ $\qquad\qquad\qquad x = 2\tan\theta$

In questions 13 to 24, find the following integrals. If you can write the answer down using the guess and check method, do so. If you need a substitution, select one for yourself!

1 3 $\displaystyle\int x\sqrt{x+1}\,dx$ $\qquad\qquad$ **1 4** $\displaystyle\int 2x\sqrt{2x-3}\,dx$

1 5 $\displaystyle\int x^2\sqrt{x^3-2}\,dx$ $\qquad\qquad$ **1 6** $\displaystyle\int (x+2)\sqrt{4x+3}\,dx$

1 7 $\displaystyle\int \frac{dx}{\sqrt{2+3x}}$ $\qquad\qquad$ **1 8** $\displaystyle\int \frac{x\,dx}{\sqrt{3-x}}$

1 9 $\displaystyle\int \frac{dx}{\sqrt{1-x^2}}$ $\qquad\qquad$ **2 0** $\displaystyle\int \frac{dx}{25+x^2}$

2 1 $\displaystyle\int \frac{x\,dx}{25+x^2}$ $\qquad\qquad$ **2 2** $\displaystyle\int \frac{x^2\,dx}{25+x^2}$

2 3 $\displaystyle\int \frac{x\,dx}{\sqrt{3-x^2}}$ $\qquad\qquad$ **2 4** $\displaystyle\int \frac{dx}{\sqrt{3-x^2}}$

In questions 25 to 30, you are given a definite integral and a substitution. Give the new values of the limits. Give the lower limit, then the upper limit. Do not work them out at this stage, but keep your answers for questions 31 to 36.

2 5 $\displaystyle\int_0^{\frac{1}{2}} \frac{1}{\sqrt{1-x^2}}\,dx$ $\quad x = \sin\theta$ $\quad$ **2 6** $\displaystyle\int_0^1 (1+x)\sqrt{1-x}\,dx$ $\quad y = 1-x$

2 7 $\displaystyle\int_0^2 \frac{1}{4+x^2}\,dx$ $\quad x = 2\tan\theta$ $\quad$ **2 8** $\displaystyle\int_0^1 \frac{x\,dx}{\sqrt{3+x}}$ $\quad z = 3+x$

2 9 $\displaystyle\int_0^1 \frac{x^2\,dx}{9+x^2}$ $\quad x = 3\tan\theta$ $\quad$ **3 0** $\displaystyle\int_0^1 \frac{x\,dx}{\sqrt{x}-3}$ $\quad z = \sqrt{x}-3$

In questions 31 to 36, find the definite integrals.

3 1 $\displaystyle\int_0^{\frac{1}{2}} \frac{1}{\sqrt{1-x^2}}\,dx$ $\qquad\qquad$ **3 2** $\displaystyle\int_0^1 (1+x)\sqrt{1-x}\,dx$

3 3 $\displaystyle\int_0^2 \frac{1}{4+x^2}\,dx$ $\qquad\qquad$ **3 4** $\displaystyle\int_0^1 \frac{x\,dx}{\sqrt{3+x}}$

3 5 $\displaystyle\int_0^1 \frac{x^2\,dx}{9+x^2}$ $\qquad\qquad$ **3 6** $\displaystyle\int_0^1 \frac{x\,dx}{\sqrt{x}-3}$

10 Integration by parts

You will need to know

● the rule, usually written as $\int u \dfrac{dv}{dx} dx = uv - \int v \dfrac{du}{dx} dx$, for integrating by parts.

The rule for integrating by parts comes from reversing the product rule for differentiation. To use the rule, you need to identify u and $\dfrac{dv}{dx}$ in the formula above.

1 Find the integral $\int x \sin x \, dx$.

Identify u and $\dfrac{dv}{dx}$.	Let $u = x$ and $\dfrac{dv}{dx} = \sin x$.
Find $\dfrac{du}{dx}$ and v to use in the formula.	Then $\dfrac{du}{dx} = 1$ and $v = -\cos x$.

You do not need to worry about a constant of integration at this stage. If you are worried by this, try it and see what happens.

Substitute for $\dfrac{du}{dx}$ and v in the formula.	$\int x \sin x \, dx = x(-\cos x) - \int (-\cos x) \, dx$ $= -x\cos x + \int \cos x \, dx.$

You can see that, if you can integrate the new integral, in this case $\int \cos x \, dx$, you can integrate the original integral.

You can now integrate $\int \cos x \, dx$, and finish off the integration.	$\int x \sin x \, dx = -x\cos x + \int \cos x \, dx$ $= -x\cos x + \sin x + C.$

Put in the constant of integration at this last stage.

Help yourself to integration

The purpose of integration by parts is to transform an awkward integral into something which is easier to integrate.

2   Find the integral $\int xe^{-x}\,dx$.

Identify u and $\dfrac{dv}{dx}$.	Let $u = x$ and $\dfrac{dv}{dx} = e^{-x}$.
Find $\dfrac{du}{dx}$ and v to use in the formula.	Then $\dfrac{du}{dx} = 1$ and $v = -e^{-x}$.
Substitute for $\dfrac{du}{dx}$ and v in the formula.	$\int xe^{-x}\,dx = x\left(-e^{-x}\right) - \int \left(-e^{-x}\right)dx$ $= -xe^{-x} + \int e^{-x}\,dx$ $= -xe^{-x} - e^{-x} + C.$

Sometimes the integral that you need to find after the first step may be easier, but need another integration by parts.

3   Find the integral $\int x^2 e^x\,dx$.

Identify u and $\dfrac{dv}{dx}$.	Let $u = x^2$ and $\dfrac{dv}{dx} = e^x$.
Find $\dfrac{du}{dx}$ and v.	Then $\dfrac{du}{dx} = 2x$ and $v = e^x$.
Substitute for $\dfrac{du}{dx}$ and v.	$\int x^2 e^x\,dx = x^2 e^x - \int 2xe^x\,dx.$

At this stage the transformed integral is easier than the original, but you still cannot integrate it yet. However, you can use integration by parts again.

Identify u and $\dfrac{dv}{dx}$ for $\int 2xe^x \, dx$.

Let $u = 2x$ and $\dfrac{dv}{dx} = e^x$.

Find $\dfrac{du}{dx}$ and v.

Then $\dfrac{du}{dx} = 2$ and $v = e^x$.

Substitute for $\dfrac{du}{dx}$ and v.

$\int 2xe^x \, dx = 2xe^x - \int 2e^x \, dx$

$= 2xe^x - 2e^x + C.$

Put this result into the result $\int x^2e^x \, dx = x^2e^x - \int 2xe^x \, dx.$

$\int x^2e^x \, dx = x^2e^x - \int 2xe^x \, dx$

$= x^2e^x - 2xe^x + 2e^x - C.$

If you make a poor choice of u and $\dfrac{dv}{dx}$, you can transform the integral, but not in a helpful way.

4 Find the integral $\int x \cos x \, dx$.

Identify u and $\dfrac{dv}{dx}$.

Let $u = \cos x$ and $\dfrac{dv}{dx} = x$.

Find $\dfrac{du}{dx}$ and v.

Then $\dfrac{du}{dx} = -\sin x$ and $v = \tfrac{1}{2}x^2$.

Substitute for $\dfrac{du}{dx}$ and v.

$\int x \cos x \, dx$

$= \tfrac{1}{2}x^2 \cos x - \int \tfrac{1}{2}x^2(-\sin x)\, dx$

$= \tfrac{1}{2}x^2 \cos x + \tfrac{1}{2}\int x^2 \sin x \, dx.$

The final result is correct, but unhelpful, because the final integral is more difficult than the original. Under these circumstances the best policy is to start again with new choices for u and $\dfrac{dv}{dx}$.

Generally, if one of the terms of the product to be integrated is a power of x, then generally this power of x should be put equal to u and therefore be differentiated when the formula is applied. This will usually make the second integral easier.

5   Find the integral $\displaystyle\int \ln x \, dx$.

At first sight it appears that you do not have a product to integrate, but there is one choice for u and dv. A similar method works for $\displaystyle\int \ln x$ and $\displaystyle\int \sin^{-1} x$.

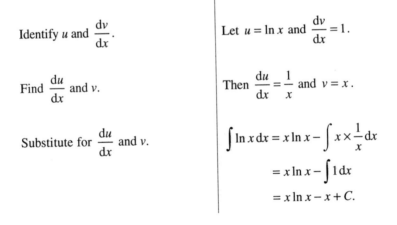

Identify u and $\dfrac{dv}{dx}$.   Let $u = \ln x$ and $\dfrac{dv}{dx} = 1$.

Find $\dfrac{du}{dx}$ and v.   Then $\dfrac{du}{dx} = \dfrac{1}{x}$ and $v = x$.

Substitute for $\dfrac{du}{dx}$ and v. $\displaystyle\int \ln x \, dx = x \ln x - \int x \times \dfrac{1}{x} \, dx$

$$= x \ln x - \int 1 \, dx$$

$$= x \ln x - x + C.$$

In Example 6, you need a trick to finish the integration by parts.

6   Find the integral $\displaystyle\int e^x \sin x \, dx$.

Identify u and $\dfrac{dv}{dx}$.   Let $u = \sin x$ and $\dfrac{dv}{dx} = e^x$.

Find $\dfrac{du}{dx}$ and v.   Then $\dfrac{du}{dx} = \cos x$ and $v = e^x$.

Substitute for $\dfrac{du}{dx}$ and v.	$\displaystyle\int e^x \sin x\, dx = e^x \sin x - \int e^x \cos x\, dx.$

This new integral doesn't look easier, but persevere.

Identify u and $\dfrac{dv}{dx}$ for the new integral.	Let $u = \cos x$ and $\dfrac{dv}{dx} = e^x$.
Find $\dfrac{du}{dx}$ and v.	Then $\dfrac{du}{dx} = -\sin x$ and $v = e^x$.
Substitute for $\dfrac{du}{dx}$ and v.	$\displaystyle\int e^x \cos x\, dx = e^x \cos x - \int e^x(-\sin x)\, dx$ $\displaystyle= e^x \cos x + \int e^x \sin x\, dx.$

You seem to have come round full circle, and arrived back with the original integral. But persevere a little further, and put the two results together.

Put the results together.	$\displaystyle\int e^x \sin x\, dx$ $\displaystyle= e^x \sin x - e^x \cos x - \int e^x \sin x\, dx.$
Add $\displaystyle\int e^x \sin x\, dx$ to both sides to solve the equation.	$\displaystyle 2\int e^x \sin x\, dx = e^x \sin x - e^x \cos x,\ \text{so}$ $\displaystyle\int e^x \sin x\, dx = \tfrac{1}{2}e^x \sin x - \tfrac{1}{2}e^x \cos x + C.$

Exercise 10

Use the method of integration by parts to find the following integrals. In some of the early questions, a hint about how to divide into parts is given.

1   $\displaystyle\int x \cos x\, dx$ Put $u = x$ and $\dfrac{dv}{dx} = \cos x$.

2   $\displaystyle\int x e^{2x}\, dx$ Put $u = x$ and $\dfrac{dv}{dx} = e^{2x}$.

Help yourself to integration

3 $\int x \cos 2x \, dx$ **4** $\int 2x e^{-2x} \, dx$

5 $\int x \ln x \, dx$

6 $\int x^2 \sin x \, dx$ You will need to integrate twice.

7 $\int x^2 e^{-x} \, dx$ You will need to integrate twice.

8 $\int x^2 \ln x \, dx$ **9** $\int \dfrac{1}{x} \ln x \, dx$

10 $\int x^2 \cos 2x \, dx$ **11** $\int x e^{-ax} \, dx$

12 $\int \sin^2 x \, dx$ **13** $\int \sin^{-1} x \, dx$

14 $\int x \tan^{-1} x \, dx$ **15** $\int \tan^{-1} x \, dx$

16 $\int \sqrt{x} \ln x \, dx$ **17** $\int e^x \cos x \, dx$

18 $\int e^{ax} \sin bx \, dx$

11 More areas and volumes

There are no new principles involved in this chapter.

You will need to know

- how to find the area between a curve and the *x*- or *y*-axis, as in Chapter 5

- how to find volumes of solids of revolution, as in Chapter 6

- how to find integrals, as in Chapters 7, 8, 9 and 10.

1   Find the area of one loop of the graph of $y = \sin x$ which is cut off by the *x*-axis.

<table>
<tr>
<td>Draw a sketch of the required region, shown in Fig. 11.1.</td>
<td>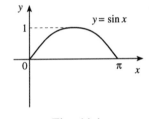</td>
</tr>
</table>

Fig. 11.1

Find where the graph cuts the *x*-axis by solving the equation $\sin x = 0$.	$\sin x = 0$ when $x = 0$ and $x = \pi$. (Remember that *x* has to be in radians for the integration.)
Identify the integral which you need to evaluate to calculate the area.	Since there are no intersections of the graph with the *x*-axis between 0 and π, the required area is $\int_0^\pi \sin x \, dx$.
Integrate.	$$\int_0^\pi \sin x \, dx = [-\cos x]_0^\pi$$ $$= (-\cos \pi) - (-\cos 0)$$ $$= -(-1) - (-1) = 2.$$
Present the answer.	The required area is 2 units.

2 Find the area of the region bounded by the curve $y = \dfrac{4}{(x-1)(x-5)}$, the x-axis

and the lines $x = 2$ and $x = 4$.

Draw a sketch of the required region, shown in Fig. 11.2.

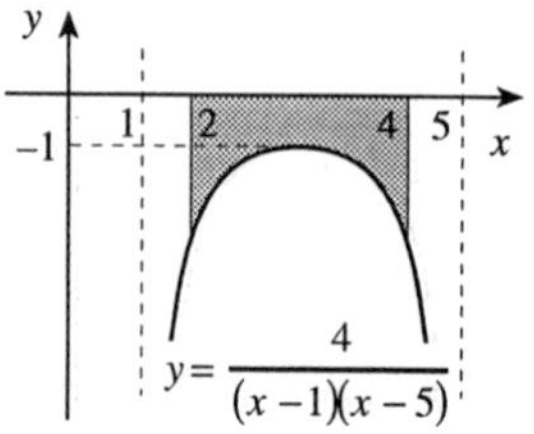

Note that the area is negative, because it is below the x-axis.

Fig. 11.2

Use the formula $\displaystyle\int_a^b f(x)\,dx$ to find the area.

The area $= \displaystyle\int_2^4 \dfrac{4}{(x-1)(x-5)}\,dx$.

You calculate this integral using the method of partial fractions.

Area $= \displaystyle\int_2^4 \left(\dfrac{1}{x-5} - \dfrac{1}{x-1}\right)dx$

Integrate.

$= \left[\ln|x-5| - \ln|x-1|\right]_2^4$

$= (\ln 1 - \ln 3) - (\ln 3 - \ln 1)$

$= -2\ln 3.$

Present the answer.

The required area is $2\ln 3$ units.

In Example 2, if you do not use the modulus of the logarithm, when you substitute the limits you get $\ln(-3)$, which is meaningless. It is important to include the modulus.

3 Find the volume of revolution when the part of the curve $y = \dfrac{1}{\sqrt{x}}$ between $x = 1$

and $x = 2$ is rotated around the x-axis.

Use the formula $\pi\displaystyle\int_a^b y^2\,dx$.

Volume $= \pi\displaystyle\int_1^2 y^2\,dx$

Substitute for the value of y from the equation of the curve.	$$= \pi \int_1^2 \frac{1}{x} dx = \pi \int_1^2 x^{-1} dx$$ $$= \pi \left[\ln|x| \right]_1^2$$ $$= \pi(\ln 2) - \pi(\ln 1)$$ $$= \pi \ln 2.$$
Present your result.	The required volume is $\pi \ln 2$ units.

4   Find the volume of revolution when the part of the curve $y = e^x$ between $x = 0$ and $x = 2$ is rotated around the x-axis.

Use the formula $\pi \int_a^b y^2 dx$.	$$\text{Volume} = \pi \int_0^2 y^2 dx$$
Substitute for the value of y from the equation of the curve.	$$= \pi \int_0^2 (e^x)^2 dx = \pi \int_0^2 e^{2x} dx$$ $$= \pi \left[\tfrac{1}{2} e^{2x} \right]_0^2$$ $$= \pi \left(\tfrac{1}{2} e^4 \right) - \pi \left(\tfrac{1}{2} e^0 \right)$$ $$= \tfrac{1}{2} \pi e^4 - \tfrac{1}{2} \pi$$ $$= \tfrac{1}{2} \pi (e^4 - 1).$$
Present your result.	The required volume is $\tfrac{1}{2} \pi (e^4 - 1)$ units.

5   Find the volume of revolution when the part of the curve $y = e^x$ between $x = 0$ and $x = 2$ is rotated around the y-axis.

Use the formula $\pi \int_a^b x^2 dy$.	$$\text{Volume} = \pi \int_a^b x^2 dy.$$

Help yourself to integration

Find x in terms of y to use in this formula, and find the required limits for y in this integral.	As $y = e^x$, $x = \ln y$. The appropraite y limits for the integral are $y = 1$, (when $x = 0$) and $y = e^2$, (when $x = 2$).
Put this information together.	$\text{Volume} = \pi \int_1^{e^2} (\ln y)^2 \, dy$
Integrate by parts to calculate this integral. Use $(\ln y)^2$ as one part and 1 as the other. Refer to Chapter 10 if necessary.	$= \pi \int_1^{e^2} (\ln y)^2 \, dy$ $= \pi \left(\left[y(\ln y)^2 \right]_1^{e^2} - \int_1^{e^2} 2 \ln y \, dy \right)$
Substitute the limits, and integrate by parts again.	$= \pi \left(e^2 \times 2^2 - 1 \times 0 \right)$ $- 2\pi \left(\left[y \ln y \right]_1^{e^2} - \int_1^{e^2} dy \right)$ $= 4e^2 \pi - 2\pi \left(e^2 \times 2 \right) + 2\pi \left[y \right]_1^{e^2}$ $= 2\pi \left(e^2 - 1 \right).$

Exercise 11

1 Find the area of the region enclosed between the curve $y = e^x$, the x-axis and the lines $x = 1$ and $x = 3$.

2 Find the area of the region enclosed between the curve $y = \sin^2 x$, the x-axis and the lines $x = 0$ and $x = \pi$.

3 Find the area of the region enclosed between the curve $y = \ln(2x)$, the x-axis and the lines $x = 1$ and $x = 2$.

4 Find the area of the region lying between $y = \dfrac{x}{x^2 + 1}$ and the x-axis, for values of x from 1 to 3.

5 Find the area of the region lying between $y = xe^{-x^2}$ and the x-axis, for values of x from 0 to 3.

58

6   Find the area of the region lying between $y = \dfrac{3x-8}{(x-2)(x-3)}$ and the x-axis, for values of x from −1 to 1.

7   Find the area of the region lying between $y = \dfrac{1}{1+x^2}$ and the x-axis, for values of x from −1 to 1.

8   Find the volume generated by rotating about the x-axis that part of the curve $y = \sin x$ which lies between $x = 0$ and $x = \pi$.

9   Find the volume generated by rotating about the x-axis that part of the curve $y = e^{-x}$ which lies between $x = -1$ and $x = 1$.

10   Find the volume generated by rotating about the x-axis that part of the curve $y = \ln x$ which lies between $x = 1$ and $x = 4$.

11   Find the volume generated by rotating about the x-axis that part of the curve $y = \cos x$ which lies above the line $y = \frac{1}{2}$ and between $x = -\pi$ and $x = \pi$.

12   Find the volume generated by rotating about the x-axis that part of the curve $y = \dfrac{1}{\sqrt{x^2 + 4}}$ which lies between $x = -1$ and $x = 1$.

13   Find the area of the region lying between the y-axis, the curve $y = e^{-x}$ and and the lines $y = e^{-1}$ and $y = 1$.

14   Find the area of the region lying between the y-axis, the curve $y = 1 + \ln x$ and and the lines $y = 0$ and $y = 1$.

15   Find the volume of the solid of revolution formed by rotating the part of the curve $y = \tan^{-1} x$ between $x = 0$ and $x = 1$ about the y-axis.

12 Approximate integration

You will need to know

- that not all functions can be integrated exactly

- that there are a number of elementary methods of approximate integration, including the rectangle rule, the trapezoidal (or trapezium) rule, the mid-point rule and Simpson's rule.

In this chapter there are examples of each of these four rules. You almost certainly do not need to use them all, and you should ensure that you work on the rule or rules which are appropriate for you.

Each of the rules applies to the integral $\int_a^b y\,dx$ and involves dividing the interval between the limits of integration into n equal divisions. The lower limit of integration is a, and the upper limit is b. Then let $x_0 = a$ and $x_n = b$. Each division has width $\dfrac{b-a}{n}$ which will be called h, so that $h = \dfrac{b-a}{n}$. Then $x_0 = a$, $x_1 = a + \dfrac{b-a}{n}$, $x_2 = a + 2\dfrac{b-a}{n}$, $\ldots$, $x_{n-1} = a + (n-1)\dfrac{b-a}{n}$, $x_n = b$. The y-values corresponding to these x-values will be called y_0, y_1, y_2, $\ldots$, y_{n-1}, y_n.

Each of the first three of these approximate methods will be used on $\int_0^1 x^2\,dx$ which you know to be equal to 0.333....

1 Use the rectangle rule with ten intervals to find an approximation to $\int_0^1 x^2\,dx$.

The rectangle rule is based on the geometric approximation shown in Fig. 12.1.

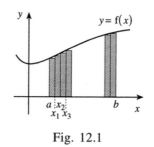

Fig. 12.1

The formula for the integral is
$$\int_a^b y\,dx = h(y_0 + y_1 + \ldots + y_{n-1}).$$

Using $a = 0$, $b = 1$, $n = 10$ and $h = 0.1$
$$\int_0^1 x^2\,dx$$
$$\approx 0.1(0 + 0.01 + 0.04 + \ldots + 0.81)$$
$$= 0.1 \times 2.85$$
$$= 0.285.$$

The rectangle rule is not particularly accurate, and you can do better without too much difficulty.

2 Use the trapezoidal rule with ten intervals to find an approximation to $\int_0^1 x^2\,dx$.

The trapezoidal rule is based on the geometric approximation shown in Fig. 12.2. Each of the shaded regions is a trapezium with its upper vertices lying on the graph.
Already you can see that it is difficult to see the difference between the area under the graph and its approximation

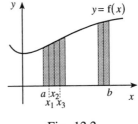

Fig. 12.2

The formula for the integral is $\int_a^b y\,dx = \tfrac{1}{2}h(y_0 + 2y_1 + \ldots + 2y_{n-1} + y_n).$

Using $a = 0$, $b = 1$, $n = 10$ and $h = 0.1$, gives
$$\int_0^1 x^2\,dx \approx \tfrac{1}{2} \times 0.1 \times \left(0 + 2(0.01 + 0.04 + \ldots + 0.81) + 1\right)$$
$$= \tfrac{1}{2} \times 0.1 \times 3.35$$
$$= 0.335.$$

As you probably expect, the trapezoidal rule is better that the rectangle rule.

It may be a surprise to know that generally the mid-point rule is better still.

3   Use the mid-point rule with ten intervals to find an approximation to $\displaystyle\int_0^1 x^2\,dx$.

The mid-point rule is based on the geometric approximation shown in Fig. 12.3. Each of the shaded regions is a rectangle so that the mid-point of its upper edge lies on the graph.

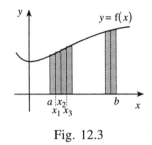

The notation $y_{\frac{1}{2}}$, $y_{\frac{3}{2}}$ etc. is used.

Fig. 12.3

The formula for the integral is $\displaystyle\int_a^b y\,dx \approx h\left(y_{\frac{1}{2}} + y_{\frac{3}{2}} + \ldots + y_{\frac{2n-3}{2}} + y_{\frac{2n-1}{2}}\right)$.

Using $a = 0$, $b = 1$, $n = 10$ and $h = 0.1$, gives

$$\int_0^1 x^2\,dx \approx 0.1 \times (0.0025 + 0.0225 + 0.1225 + \ldots + 0.9025)$$

$$= 0.1 \times$$

$$= 0.1 \times 3.325$$

$$= 0.3325.$$

The best rule is Simpson's rule, which needs an even value for n. The rule works by fitting a second degree curve (a parabola) so that it passes through the points (a, y_0), (x_1, y_1) and (x_2, y_2), and then calculates the area under this curve exactly. It then does the same through the points (x_2, y_2), (x_3, y_3) and (x_4, y_4), and so on until the whole interval of integration is covered.

No diagram is given, because it would be impossible to distinguish the curve from the approximations to it.

Simpson's rule is not used on the example $\displaystyle\int_0^1 x^2\,dx$ because it gives an exact value for the result. Instead it is used on $\displaystyle\int_0^1 x^4\,dx$, with ten intervals, as before. You know that this integral is equal to 0.2.

4   Use the Simpson's rule with ten intervals to find an approximation to $\int_0^1 x^4 \, dx$.

The formula for the integral is

$$\int_a^b y \, dx \approx \tfrac{1}{3} h\left(y_0 + 4y_1 + 2y_2 + 4y_3 + 2y_4 + \ldots + 4y_{n-1} + y_n\right).$$

Using $a = 0$, $b = 1$, $n = 10$ and $h = 0.1$, gives

$$\int_0^1 x^4 \, dx \approx \tfrac{1}{3} \times 0.1 \times \left(0 + 4\left(0.1^4 + \ldots + 0.9^4\right) + 2\left(0.2^4 + \ldots + 0.8^4\right) + 1\right)$$

$$= \tfrac{1}{3} \times 0.1 \times \left(0 + 4 \times 0.9669 + 2 \times 0.5664 + 1\right)$$

$$= \tfrac{1}{3} \times 0.1 \times 6.004$$

$$= 0.200\,013\,333.$$

As you can see Simpson's rule is very accurate indeed.

Exercise 12

For each of the following integrals, find a ten interval approximation using whichever method is appropriate to you.

1 $\int_0^1 x^3 \, dx$ **2** $\int_0^1 \sqrt{1 + x^3} \, dx$

3 $\int_0^{\frac{1}{2}\pi} \sin x \, dx$ **4** $\int_0^{\frac{1}{2}\pi} \sqrt{\sin x} \, dx$

5 $\int_0^2 \left(1 + x^2\right)^{\frac{1}{3}} \, dx$ **6** $\int_1^4 \sqrt{1 + x^2} \, dx$

13 Differential equations

You will need to know

- what a differential equation is

- how to solve differential equations in which you can separate the variables.

You first encountered differential equations in this book in Chapter 3. In the examples there you could integrate the differential equation, that is, solve it, by direct integration. In this chapter, you will see another type of differential equation, the variables separable differential equation.

A variables separable differential equation is one for which you can write the equation in the form with all the terms involving one variable on one side of the equation and the other terms on the other side.

1   Solve the differential equation $y\dfrac{dy}{dx} = x$.

<table>
<tr>
<td>This equation is variables separable, so separate the variables.</td>
<td>$y\dfrac{dy}{dx} = x$ so $y\,dy = x\,dx$.</td>
</tr>
</table>

Notice that the left-hand side contains only terms in y and the right-hand side only terms in x. This is the form with variables separated which you are aiming for in every question in this chapter.

<table>
<tr>
<td>Integrate both sides.</td>
<td>$\int y\,dy = \int x\,dx$

so $\frac{1}{2}y^2 = \frac{1}{2}x^2 + C$.</td>
</tr>
</table>

Sometimes it may be convenient to give the constant in a slightly different form. For instance, in Example 1, if the constant had been $\frac{1}{2}C$ instead of C, the solution would have appeared as $\frac{1}{2}y^2 = \frac{1}{2}x^2 + \frac{1}{2}C$, or as $y^2 = x^2 + C$. This may happen in a number of the following examples, and in the exercises.

2 Solve the differential equation $x\dfrac{dy}{dx} = y$.

This equation is variables separable, so separate the variables.	$x\dfrac{dy}{dx} = y$ so $\dfrac{dy}{y} = \dfrac{dx}{x}$.
Integrate both sides.	$\displaystyle\int \dfrac{dy}{y} = \int \dfrac{dx}{x}$ so $\ln|y| = \ln|x| + \ln C$.

Notice that in this case, the constant is given as $\ln C$.

Simplify the solution.	$y = Cx$, where C is a positive or negative constant.

A common type of equation describes growth. Examples 3 and 4 are of this type.

3 Solve the differential equation $\dfrac{dx}{dt} = 2x$.

Separate the variables.	$\dfrac{dx}{dt} = 2x$ so $\dfrac{dx}{x} = 2dt$.
Integrate both sides.	$\displaystyle\int \dfrac{dx}{x} = \int 2\,dt$ so $\ln|x| = 2t + \ln C$.
Simplify the solution.	$|x| = Ce^{2t}$.

In the kind of equation in Example 3, it often occurs that x is strictly positive; in this case the solution would be $x = Ce^{2t}$.

4 Solve the differential equation $\dfrac{dx}{dt} = kx + m$, where k and m are positive constants.

Separate the variables.	$\dfrac{dx}{dt} = kx + m$ so $\dfrac{dx}{kx+m} = dt$.
Integrate both sides.	$\displaystyle\int \dfrac{dx}{kx+m} = \int dt$ so $\dfrac{1}{k}\ln\lvert kx+m \rvert = t + \dfrac{1}{k}\ln C$.

Note the form of the constant in this case.

Simplify the solution.	$\ln\lvert kx+m \rvert = kt + \ln C$, so $\lvert kx+m \rvert = Ce^{kt}$.
If x is to be positive, as is quite likely, then you can drop the modulus signs.	Then $kx + m = Ce^{kt}$, or $x = \dfrac{C}{k}e^{kt} - \dfrac{m}{k}$.

This kind of equation can also describe decay.

5 Solve the differential equation $\dfrac{dx}{dt} = -3x$.

Separate the variables.	$\dfrac{dx}{dt} = -3x$ so $\dfrac{dx}{x} = -3\,dt$.
Integrate both sides.	$\displaystyle\int \dfrac{dx}{x} = \int -3\,dt$ so $\ln\lvert x \rvert = -3t + \ln C$.
Simplify the solution.	$\ln\lvert x \rvert = -3t + \ln C$, so $\lvert x \rvert = Ce^{-3t}$.

| If x is to be positive, you can drop the modulus signs. | Then $x = Ce^{-3t}$. |

6 Solve the differential equation $x\dfrac{dy}{dx} = y(y+1)$, given that when $x = 1$, $y = 2$.

Separate the variables.	$x\dfrac{dy}{dx} = y(y+1)$ so $\dfrac{dy}{y(y+1)} = \dfrac{dx}{x}$.
Integrate both sides. You need partial fractions for the left-hand side.	$\displaystyle\int \dfrac{dy}{y(y+1)} = \int \dfrac{dx}{x}$, so $\displaystyle\int\left(\dfrac{1}{y} - \dfrac{1}{y+1}\right)dy = \int \dfrac{dx}{x}$ and $\ln\|y\| - \ln\|y+1\| = \ln\|x\| + \ln C$.
Simplify the solution.	$\ln\left\|\dfrac{y}{y+1}\right\| = \ln\|x\| + \ln C$.
Substitute $x = 1$, $y = 2$ to find C.	$\ln\left\|\dfrac{2}{3}\right\| = \ln\|1\| + \ln C$ so $C = \tfrac{2}{3}$.
Present the solution.	$\left\|\dfrac{y}{y+1}\right\| = \left\|\dfrac{2x}{3}\right\|$.

Exercise 13

In questions 1 to 8, solve the following differential equations, giving the constant in a convenient form. You may need to give your answer as an implicit equation relating x and y, rather than as an equation in the form $y = \ldots$.

1 $\dfrac{dy}{dx} = \tfrac{1}{2}y$

2 $\dfrac{dy}{dx} = -y$

3 $\dfrac{dy}{dx} = xy$

4 $\dfrac{dy}{dx} = -xy$

5 $\dfrac{dy}{dx} = \dfrac{\sin x}{\cos y}$ **6** $\dfrac{dy}{dx} = xe^{-y}$

7 $\dfrac{dy}{dx} = \dfrac{2xy}{x^2 + 1}$ **8** $\dfrac{dy}{dx} = \dfrac{\tan x}{\tan y}$

In questions 9 to 16, solve the given differential equation, using the initial condition to determine the value of the constant. You may need to give your answer as an implicit equation relating x and y, rather than as an equation in the form $y = \ldots$.

9 $\dfrac{dy}{dx} = 3$ when $x = 0$, $y = 2$

10 $\dfrac{dy}{dx} = -1$ when $x = -1$, $y = -2$

11 $\dfrac{dy}{dx} = xy - x$ when $x = 0$, $y = 1$

12 $x\dfrac{dy}{dx} = 2y$ when $x = 1$, $y = 2$

13 $2y\dfrac{dy}{dx} = e^x\left(y^2 - 1\right)$ when $x = 0$, $y = \sqrt{2}$

14 $y\dfrac{dy}{dx} = 10$ when $x = 0$, $y = 30$

15 $\tan x\dfrac{dy}{dx} = \tan y$ when $x = \frac{1}{6}\pi$, $y = \frac{1}{2}\pi$

16 $\dfrac{1}{\sqrt{x}}\dfrac{dy}{dx} = x - 1$ when $x = 1$, $y = -\frac{4}{15}$

14 More differential equations

You will need to know

- how to solve differential equations in which you can separate the variables

- that the rate of change of a quantity q is given by $\dfrac{dq}{dt}$

- that velocity $v = \dfrac{ds}{dt}$ and acceleration $a = \dfrac{dv}{dt} = \dfrac{d^2 s}{dt^2} = v \dfrac{dv}{ds}$

- how to construct a differential equation from information about rate of change.

1   For all values of x the gradient of a graph is given by $2e^{2x}$. The graph passes through $(0, e)$. Find its equation, and find the value of y when $x = 1$.

Use the information about the gradient to write down a differential equation.	Gradient $= \dfrac{dy}{dx}$, so $\dfrac{dy}{dx} = 2e^{2x}$.
Integrate the equation.	$y = e^{2x} + C$.
Use the information that the graph passes through $(0, e)$ to find the value of the constant C.	When $x = 0$, $y = e$, so $e = e^0 + C$ or $e = 1 + C$, giving $C = e - 1$.
Put this value of C in the equation.	The equation is $y = e^{2x} + e - 1$.
Use the equation to find the value of y when $x = 1$.	When $x = 1$, $y = e^2 + e - 1$

Most differential equations will involve a rate of change rather than a gradient, and are likely to require you to write down an equation given information about the rate of change.

In Example 2, the equation is given to you.

2 The number of insects in a colony is N. The insects breed in such a way that the rate of increase of N per day is $0.1N$. The initial value of N is 1000. Find the value of t when $N = 2000$.

Construct an equation from the information about the rate of change.	The rate of change of N is $\dfrac{dN}{dt}$ so $\dfrac{dN}{dt} = 0.1N$, that is, $\dfrac{dN}{N} = 0.1\,dt$.
Integrate both sides.	$\displaystyle\int \dfrac{dN}{N} = \int 0.1\,dt$ so $\ln\lvert N \rvert = 0.1t + \ln C$, and since $N > 0$, $N = Ce^{0.1t}$.
Use the initial condition to find the value of the constant C.	When $t = 0$, $N = 1000$, so $1000 = C$, and $N = 1000e^{0.1t}$.
Use this equation to find what you need.	When $N = 2000$, let the time $t = T$, so $2000 = 1000e^{0.1T}$ and $2 = e^{0.1T}$. Taking logarithms, $0.1T = \ln 2$ or $T = 10\ln 2$.
The question needs a numerical answer.	The population is 2000 after about 6.93 days.

3 The acceleration of a particle which is moving in a straight line is given by $-\omega^2 x$, where x is the distance from a point on the line, and ω is a constant. When $v = 0$, $x = a$. Find an expression for the velocity.

When you are given the acceleration, you need to decide whether to use $a = \dfrac{dv}{dt}$ or $a = \dfrac{d^2x}{dt^2}$ or $a = v\dfrac{dv}{dx}$. If the acceleration is given in terms of x, use $a = v\dfrac{dv}{dx}$. If the acceleration is given in terms of t use $a = \dfrac{dv}{dt}$ or $a = \dfrac{d^2x}{dt^2}$. If v is required, use $\dfrac{dv}{dt}$; if x is required, it is usually better to use $a = \dfrac{d^2x}{dt^2}$, but sometimes it is better to use $a = v\dfrac{dv}{dx}$ to find v, and then to substitute $v = \dfrac{dx}{dt}$ to find x.

Write down an equation from the information about the acceleration.	$a = v\dfrac{dv}{dx} = -\omega^2 x.$
This equation is variables separable, so separate the variables and integrate.	$v\,dv = -\omega^2 x\,dx$ so $\displaystyle\int v\,dv = \int -\omega^2 x\,dx$ and $\frac{1}{2}v^2 = -\frac{1}{2}\omega^2 x^2 + C.$
Use the given information to find C.	When $v = 0,\ x = a$, so $0 = -\frac{1}{2}\omega^2 a^2 + C$ and $C = \frac{1}{2}\omega^2 a^2.$
Present your result.	$\frac{1}{2}v^2 = \frac{1}{2}\omega^2 a^2 - \frac{1}{2}\omega^2 x^2$, so $v^2 = \omega^2 a^2 - \omega^2 x^2 = \omega^2\left(a^2 - x^2\right).$

When the rate of change of something is negative, the quantity is decaying.

4   The rate of loss of temperature per minute of a cup of coffee is $k(\theta - 20)$ where θ is the temperature in degrees Centigrade, and k is a constant. Initially the temperature is $70°$, and after 10 minutes the temperature is $50°$. Find an equation for the temperature in terms of time.

Construct an equation from the information about the rate of change.	$\dfrac{d\theta}{dt} = -k(\theta - 20).$

The negative sign arises because $\dfrac{d\theta}{dt}$ represents the rate of increase of temperature, and the information given is about the loss of temperature.

This equation is variables separable, so separate the variables and integrate.	$\displaystyle\int \frac{d\theta}{(\theta-20)} = \int -k\,dt$ so $\ln\lvert\theta-20\rvert = -kt + \ln C.$
Use the given information to find C.	When $t=0$, $\theta=70$, so $\ln 50 = \ln C$ and $\ln\lvert\theta-20\rvert = -kt + \ln 50$, giving $\theta = 20 + 50e^{-kt}.$
You can find k by using the other piece of information.	When $t=10$, $\theta = 50$ so $50 = 20 + 50e^{-10k}$ giving $0.6 = e^{-10k}$ and $k = -\frac{1}{10}\ln 0.6$ or $k = \frac{1}{10}\ln\frac{5}{3}.$
Present your result.	The temperature $\theta\,^{\circ}C$ is given by $\theta = 20 + 50e^{-t\frac{1}{10}\ln\frac{5}{3}}.$

Exercise 14

1   The gradient at any point on a curve is given by $-\dfrac{x}{y}$. The curve passes through $(3,4)$. Find its equation.

2   The gradient at any point on a curve is given by $\dfrac{y}{x}$. The curve passes through $(1,2)$. Find its equation.

3   The rate of growth of a population p of bacteria is given by $2p$ per hour. Initially the population is 1000. Find when the population has doubled correct to the nearest minute.

4   Radioactive substances decay in such a way that their rate of decay is proportional to the amount present at that time. Let q be the quantity of radioactive substance present at any time. Suppose that the initial amount of q present is 1000 gm and that the amount present after 1 year is 500 gm. Find an equation for q in terms of time.

5   The velocity $v\,\mathrm{m\,s^{-1}}$ of a body moving in a straight line is given by $v = 3\sin 2t$, where t seconds is the time from the moment when it passed through a fixed point O. Find the distance of the particle from the fixed point at time t seconds.

6   The temperature of a hot-plate is falling at a rate proportional to the excess temperature of the hot-plate above its surroundings. Initially the temperature above the surroundings is $300\,^{\circ}C$, and the temperature is down to $200\,^{\circ}C$ after 5 minutes. Find the time, to the nearest minute, when the temperature is only $20\,^{\circ}C$ above the temperature of the surroundings.

7   A colony of insects initially has 1000 insects. The rate of growth of the number N of insects at time t days is given by $kN(M - N)$ where k and M are positive constants, and $M > N$. Find an expression for N in terms of k, M and t.

15 Revision exercises

Revision exercise 1

1 Integrate $3x+1$, $\left(x^2+1\right)^2$ and $\sqrt{x}$.

2 Given that $\dfrac{dy}{dx} = 2x+1$, and that when $x=2$, $y=3$, find y in terms of x.

3 Find the area of the region between the curve $y = 3x^2 + 2x - 1$, the x-axis and the lines $x=2$ and $x=4$.

4 The part of the curve bounded by $y = \sqrt{x+2}$, the lines $x=2$ and $x=7$ and the x-axis is rotated about the x-axis to form a volume of revolution. Find the volume of this solid.

5 Solve the differential equation $x\dfrac{dy}{dx} = 2y$, given that when $x=1$, $y=2$.

6 The acceleration a m s^{-2} of a particle moving in a straight line is given by $a = 2\cos 2t$. When $t=0$, the displacement is 3 m, and the velocity is 2 m s^{-1}. Find the displacement and velocity after 1 second.

Revision exercise 2

1 Integrate $\cos^2 3x$, $\left(x+\dfrac{1}{x}\right)^3$ and $\dfrac{1}{\sqrt{2x}}$.

2 Solve the differential equation $y^2\dfrac{dy}{dx} = 2x+1$, given that when $x=2$, $y=3$.

3 Use the substitution $u = \sin x$ to calculate $\displaystyle\int_0^{\frac{1}{4}\pi} \cos^3 2x \sin^2 2x \, dx$.

4 Find the area of the region bounded by the curve $y = x^3$, the y-axis and the lines $y=1$ and $y=8$.

5 The acceleration a m s^{-2} of a body moving in a straight line is given by $a = 3x^2$ where x m is the distance from the origin. When $x=1$, $v=2$. Find the velocity when $x=2$.

6 The part of the curve with equation $y = x + \dfrac{1}{x}$ between $x=\frac{1}{2}$ and $x=2$ is rotated about the x-axis. Find the volume of the solid of revolution formed.

Revision exercise 3

1. Calculate $\int_1^2 \left(x - \dfrac{1}{x^2} \right) dx$, $\int_1^4 \dfrac{1}{\sqrt{x}}\,dx$ and $\int_1^4 \dfrac{1}{x}\,dx$.

2. The acceleration a m s^{-2} of a train which starts from rest at time $t = 0$ and travels in a straight line is given by $a = 2 - \frac{1}{15}t$ for values of t lying between 0 and 60 inclusive. Find the velocity and displacement of the train after 60 seconds.

3. A curve which satisfies the differential equation $\dfrac{dy}{dx} = xy\sin x$ passes through the point $\left(\frac{1}{2}\pi, 1 \right)$. Find the equation of the curve, and the value of y when $x = \pi$.

4. The region bounded by the curves $y = x^2$ and $y = x^{\frac{1}{3}}$ is (*a*) rotated about the *x*-axis and (*b*) rotated about the *y*-axis. Find the two volumes of revolution so formed.

5. Find the area of the region bounded by the curve $y = (2 - x)\ln x$ and the *x*-axis.

6. Use integration by parts twice to calculate the integral $\int e^{ax} \sin bx\,dx$.

Revision exercise 4

1. Calculate $\int_0^{\frac{1}{2}\pi} \cos x \cos 2x\,dx$, $\int_0^{\ln 2} e^{-3x}\,dx$, $\int_0^{\frac{1}{2}\pi} x \sin 2x\,dx$.

2. The acceleration a m s^{-2} of a body falling from rest under gravity taking air resistance into account can be modelled by the equation $a = g - kv$, where g and k are constants and v m s^{-1} is the velocity. Find an equation for the velocity after time t seconds.

3. Calculate the area of the region between the curves $y = x^2$ and $y = x^3$.

4. A glass holding 0.5 litres is to be made in the form of a volume of revolution of the graph of $y = kx^2$, where k is a constant, between $x = 0$ and $x = 10$, rotated about the *y*-axis. The units are centimetres. Calculate the value of k.

5. A curve satisfies the differential equation $\left(1 + x^2 \right) \dfrac{dy}{dx} = 2xy$ and passes through the point $(1,1)$. Find its equation.

6 Use the substitution $u = 1 + x^2$ to calculate $\int_0^1 \left(x + 2x^3\right)\sqrt{\left(1 + x^2\right)}\, dx$.

Revision exercise 5

1 Calculate $\int_0^{\frac{1}{2}\pi} \sin 2x\, dx$, $\int_0^{\ln 2} x e^{-2x}\, dx$, $\int_0^{\frac{1}{4}\pi} \tan x\, dx$.

2 Find the area of the region bounded by the curve $y = (x - a)(b - x)$, where $b > a$.

3 Find the volume of the solid of revolution generated when the region bounded by the graph of $y = \cos x$ between $x = -\frac{1}{2}\pi$ and $x = \frac{1}{2}\pi$ is rotated about the x-axis.

4 Solve the differential equation $\sqrt{\left(1 - x^2\right)}\, y\, \dfrac{dy}{dx} = x$, given that when $x = 1$, $y = 1$.

5 Use integration by parts to find $\int_1^e x^n \ln x\, dx$.

6 The acceleration a m s^{-2} of a body falling from rest under gravity taking air resistance into account can be modelled by the equation $a = g - kv^2$, where g and k are constants and v m s^{-1} is the velocity. Find an equation for the velocity when the displacement is x metres.

Revision exercise 6

1 Calculate $\int_0^{\pi} \cos^2 x\, dx$, $\int_0^2 (1 + 4x)^{\frac{3}{2}}\, dx$, $\int_0^{\ln 2} x e^{-x}\, dx$.

2 The region between the curve $y = x^2$, the x-axis, the origin and the line $x = k$, where $k > 1$ is rotated about the x-axis to form a volume of revolution. The volume between $x = 0$ and $x = 1$ is exactly half of the volume of the total solid. Find the value of k.

3 Find the area of the region between the curve $y = x^2 - 3x + 2$ and the straight line $y = 2x - 2$.

4 Use the method of integration by substitution to find $\int \dfrac{2e^{2x}}{2 + 3e^{2x}}\, dx$.

5 The temperature $\theta\,°C$ of a cup of tea t minutes after it was made is given by the differential equation $\dfrac{d\theta}{dt} = -k(\theta - 20)$. Initially the tea is at temperature

$70\,°C$ and 5 minutes later the temperature is $50\,°C$. Find when the temperature is at $40\,°C$.

6   Solve the differential equation $\dfrac{dy}{dx} = 2y + 3$, given that when $x = 0$, $y = -2$.

Revision exercise 7

1   Calculate $\displaystyle\int_{-1}^{-e} \ln(-x)\,dx$, $\displaystyle\int_{0}^{2\pi} \sin^2 4x\,dx$, $\displaystyle\int_{-1}^{-3} \frac{1}{2x+1}\,dx$.

2   Use the substitution $x = \dfrac{\sqrt{3}}{2}\sin\theta$ to integrate $\displaystyle\int \frac{1}{\sqrt{3-4x^2}}\,dx$.

3   The region shaded in Fig. 15.1 below lies between the curves $y^2 = x$ and $y^2 = x - 2$. Find its area.

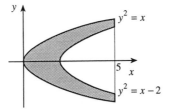

Fig. 15.1

4   In Fig. 15.1, the shaded region is rotated about the x-axis to form a volume of revolution. Find its volume.

5   A curve which satisfies the differential equation $\dfrac{y}{x}\dfrac{dy}{dx} = \dfrac{1+y^2}{1+x^2}$ passes through the point $(2,3)$. Find its equation.

6   A particle moves in a straight line in such a way that its retardation is always proportional to x^2 where x is the displacement from the origin O. When $x = 1$, the velocity $v = 0$, and when $x = 0$, $v = 2$. Find v in terms of x.

16 Answers

In these answers, C stands for an arbitrary constant.

Exercise 2, page 6

1 $\frac{1}{3}x^3 + C$

2 $x^3 + C$

3 $\frac{5}{3}x^3 + C$

4 $\frac{1}{5}x^5 + C$

5 $x^5 + C$

6 $\frac{3}{5}x^5 + C$

7 $\frac{1}{2}x^2 + C$

8 $x^2 + C$

9 $\frac{3}{2}x^2 + C$

10 $5x + C$

11 $\frac{1}{4}x^2 + C$

12 $\frac{1}{6}x^3 + C$

13 $-\frac{1}{16}x^4 + C$

14 $-x^{-1} + C$

15 $x^{-2} + C$

16 $-\frac{1}{5}x^{-5} + C$

17 $\frac{3}{4}x^4 + C$

18 $\frac{1}{12}x^4 + C$

19 $-\frac{3}{2}x^{-2} + C$

20 $x^{-3} + C$

21 $\frac{1}{2}x^{-4} + C$

22 C

23 $2x^2 - 3x + C$

24 $\frac{1}{2}x^2 + x + C$

25 $2x^3 - x^2 + x + C$

26 $2x - 3x^2 + C$

27 $\frac{3}{2}x^2 - \frac{1}{3}x^3 + C$

28 $3x^3 + 8x + C$

29 $\frac{1}{3}x^3 + x^{-1} + C$

30 $\frac{1}{4}x^4 - \frac{1}{2}x^{-2} + C$

31 $\frac{1}{4}x^4 + \frac{1}{3}x^3 + \frac{1}{2}x^2 + x + C$

32 $\frac{1}{8}x^4 + \frac{1}{9}x^3 + \frac{1}{8}x^2 + \frac{1}{5}x + C$

33 $x^6 - x^4 - x^2 + 3x + C$

34 $\frac{1}{8}x^4 - \frac{1}{9}x^3 + C$

35 $-2x^{-1} + \frac{5}{2}x^{-2} + C$

36 $-5x^{-1} + 3x^{-2} - 2x^{-3} + C$

37 $\frac{2}{3}x^{\frac{3}{2}} + C$

38 $\frac{4}{3}x^{\frac{3}{2}} + C$

39 $x^{\frac{3}{2}} + C$

40 $-4x^{\frac{1}{2}} + C$

41 $\frac{6}{5}x^{\frac{5}{3}} + C$

42 $9x^{\frac{1}{3}} + C$

43 $\frac{2}{3}x^{\frac{3}{2}} + C$

44 $4x^{\frac{1}{2}} + C$

45 $2x^{\frac{3}{2}} + C$

46 $\dfrac{2\sqrt{3}}{3}x^{\frac{3}{2}} + C$

47 $\dfrac{4}{\sqrt{2}}x^{\frac{1}{2}} + C$ or $2\sqrt{2}x^{\frac{1}{2}} + C$ **48** $\frac{1}{3}x^3 + 2x^2 + 4x + C$

49 $2x^3 + \frac{13}{2}x^2 + 6x + C$ **50** $\frac{1}{2}x^2 - 4x^{\frac{1}{2}} - x^{-1} + C$

51 $x^3 + x^2 - x + C$ **52** $\frac{1}{5}x^5 + \frac{1}{2}x^4 + C$

53 $\frac{2}{5}x^{\frac{5}{2}} + \frac{4}{3}x^{\frac{3}{2}} + C$ **54** $\frac{2}{5}x^{\frac{5}{2}} + x^2 + \frac{2}{3}x^{\frac{3}{2}} + C$

55 $\frac{2}{3}x^{\frac{3}{2}} + 2x + 2x^{\frac{1}{2}} + C$ **56** $\frac{1}{2}x^2 - x^{-1} + C$

57 $-x^{-1} - \frac{3}{2}x^{-2} - \frac{2}{3}x^{-3} + C$ **58** $\frac{8}{5}x^{\frac{5}{2}} - 2x^{\frac{1}{2}} + C$

59 $8x^{\frac{1}{2}} - 4x^{-\frac{1}{2}} + C$ **60** $-16x^{-\frac{1}{2}} - \frac{2\sqrt{2}}{3}x^{-\frac{3}{2}} + C$

Exercise 3, page 9

1 $u = 2v^2 - 3v + 3$ **2** $y = x^2 + 3x - 7$

3 $y = 3x + 7$ **4** $w = 3u^3 + 3u^2 - 3u + 29$

5 $y = -3x + 13$ **6** $y = -\frac{1}{2}x^2 + 2x - 3$

7 $(-2, -16)$ **8** $y = \frac{1}{3}x^3 - 2x + \frac{4}{3}$

9 $y = x^2 + \dfrac{1}{x} + 1$ **10** $y = 5x - 3x^2$

11 $y = x^3 - 3x^2 - 2x$ **12** $(-3, 14)$

13 $y = 1 + 3x + 4x^2 - 2x^3$ **14** $(2, 0)$ and $(-5, 0)$

15 $y = x^3 - 2x^2 - \dfrac{2}{x} - 3$ **16** $y = 2x^{\frac{3}{2}} - 10$

Exercise 4, page 14

1 $s = 6 + 36t - 2t^2$ **2** $s = 48t - \frac{3}{2}t^2$, 32 seconds

3 $v = t^2 + t + 5$ **4**   13.5 m

5 $h = 147t - 4.9t^2$, 1102.5 m   **6** $v = 9t - 2t^2 + 3$

7 $s = 12t - \frac{1}{9}t^3$, 6 s, 48 m   **8**   3 m, 3 m, 39 m

9 $v = 58.8 - 9.8t$, $h = 58.8t - 4.9t^2$, 171.5 m, 171.5 m. After 5 and 7 seconds the

     particle is at the same height, once on the way up and once on the way down.

Exercise 5, page 20

1	$2\frac{1}{3}$	**2**	60
3	16	**4**	−37
5	−50	**6**	15
7	375	**8**	162
9	$2\frac{1}{2}$	**10**	−1
11	115	**12**	39
13	$13\frac{2}{3}$	**14**	−6
15	$8\frac{2}{3}$	**16**	24

17 22 **18** $9\frac{1}{3}$

19 $21\frac{1}{3}$ **20** $4\frac{1}{2}$

21 $57\frac{1}{6}$ **22** $11\frac{1}{6}$

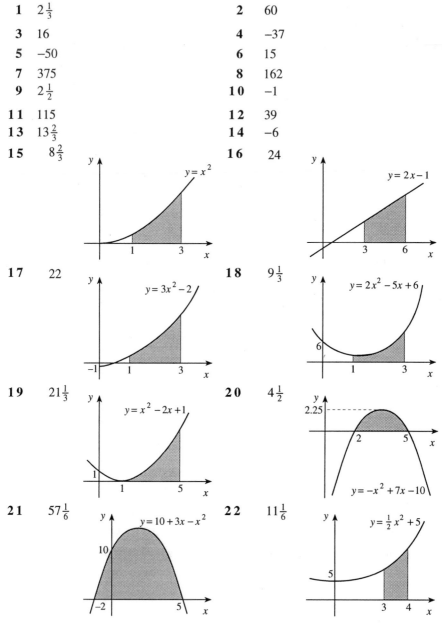

23   55

24 $21\frac{3}{10}$

25   36

26   150

27 $57\frac{1}{6}$

28 $10\frac{2}{3}$

29   36

30 $4\frac{1}{2}$

31 $10\frac{2}{3}$

32 $4\frac{1}{2}$

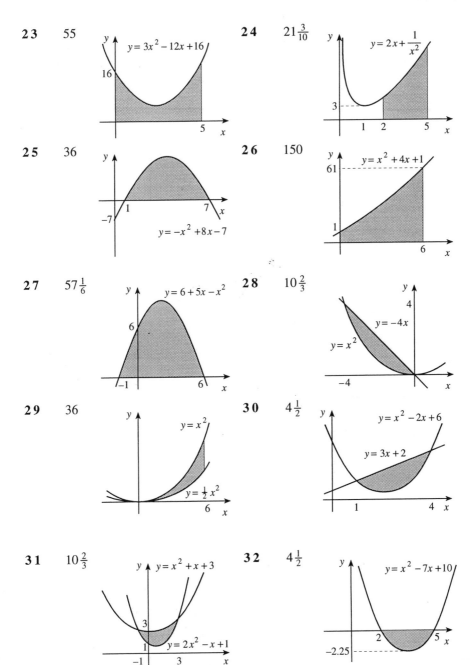

$y = 3x^2 - 12x + 16$

$y = 2x + \dfrac{1}{x^2}$

$y = -x^2 + 8x - 7$

$y = x^2 + 4x + 1$

$y = 6 + 5x - x^2$

$y = -4x$

$y = x^2$

$y = x^2$

$y = \frac{1}{2}x^2$

$y = x^2 - 2x + 6$

$y = 3x + 2$

$y = x^2 + x + 3$

$y = 2x^2 - x + 1$

$y = x^2 - 7x + 10$

33   0

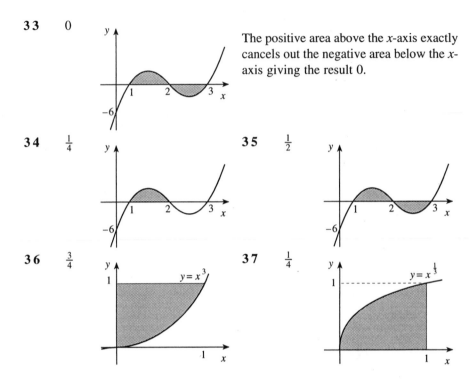

The positive area above the *x*-axis exactly cancels out the negative area below the *x*-axis giving the result 0.

34 $\frac{1}{4}$

35 $\frac{1}{2}$

36 $\frac{3}{4}$

37 $\frac{1}{4}$

Exercise 6, page 25

1 34π

2 $\frac{27}{5}\pi$

3 $\frac{500}{3}\pi$

4 14π

5 36π

6 7π

7 $\frac{1}{30}\pi$

8 $\frac{25}{3}\pi$

9 $\frac{70}{3}\pi$

10 $\frac{81}{10}\pi$

11 $\frac{128}{5}\pi$

12 $\frac{1023}{5}\pi$

13 $\frac{3}{10}\pi$

14 $\frac{2}{15}\pi$

Exercise 7, page 33

In some cases, where space permits, alternative answers are given.

1 $\frac{3}{5}x^5 + C$ **2** $\frac{1}{3}x^6 + C$

3 $8\sqrt{x} + C$ or $8x^{\frac{1}{2}} + C$ **4** $-2x^{-1} + C$ or $-\dfrac{2}{x} + C$

5 $\frac{1}{3}x^3 + \frac{1}{5}x^5 + C$ **6** $\frac{1}{2}x^2 + \ln|x| + C$

7 $\frac{2}{3}x^{\frac{3}{2}} + \frac{1}{2}x^2 + C$ **8** $\ln|x| - x^{-1} + C$ or $\ln|x| - \dfrac{1}{x} + C$

9 $\frac{4}{3}x^3 - 25x + C$ **10** $\frac{1}{2}x^2 + 2x + \ln|x| + C$

11 $2\ln|x| + C$ or $\ln(x^2) + C$ **12** $\frac{1}{2}\ln|x| + C$ or $\ln\left(x^{\frac{1}{2}}\right) + C$

13 $-\ln|x| + C$ or $\ln\left|\dfrac{1}{x}\right| + C$ **14** $-2\ln|x| + C$ or $\ln\left(\dfrac{1}{x^2}\right) + C$

15 $-\cos x + C$ **16** $-\sin x + C$

17 $\frac{2}{3}e^{3x} + C$ **18** $2e^{2x} + C$

19 $-\frac{3}{2}e^{-2x} + C$ **20** $-e^{-2x} + C$

21 $-e^{-x} + C$ **22** $\dfrac{1}{a}e^{ax+b} + C$

23 $3e^{\frac{1}{3}x} + C$ **24** $4e^{-\frac{1}{2}x} + C$

25 $e^x - e^{-x} + 2x + C$ **26** $e^x - e^{-x} - 2x + C$

27 $\frac{1}{18}(3x+2)^6 + C$ **28** $\frac{1}{4}(x+2)^4 + C$

29 $-\frac{1}{7}(1-x)^7 + C$ **30** $-\frac{1}{9}(5-3x)^3 + C$

31 $-\frac{1}{2}(1+2x)^{-1} + C$ or $\dfrac{-1}{2(1+2x)} + C$ **32** $\frac{1}{2}(1-2x)^{-3} + C$ or $\dfrac{1}{2(1-2x)^3} + C$

33 $4\left(1+\frac{1}{3}x\right)^{\frac{3}{2}} + C$ **34** $16\left(1+\frac{1}{4}x\right)^{\frac{1}{2}} + C$ or $8\sqrt{4+x} + C$

35 $\frac{1}{2}\sin 2x + C$ **36** $-\cos 4x + C$

37 $\cos(-2x) + C$ **38** $\dfrac{2}{\pi}\sin\left(\frac{1}{2}\pi x\right) + C$

39 $-\frac{1}{2}\cos(x^2) + C$ **40** $-\frac{1}{\pi}\cos(\frac{1}{2}\pi x) + C$

41 $-\frac{1}{a}\cos(ax + b) + C$ **42** $\frac{1}{\omega}\sin\omega(x - \frac{1}{4}\pi) + C$

43 $2\ln|1 + x| + C$ **44** $\ln|2 + 3x| + C$

45 $\ln|1 - x| + C$ **46** $\ln|x - 1| + C$

47 $\frac{1}{6}\ln|1 + 3x| + C$ **48** $-\ln|4 - 5x| + C$

49 $-\frac{1}{7}\ln|1 - 7x| + C$ **50** $-3\ln|2 - 3x| + C$

51 $-\ln|1 - x^2| + C$ **52** $\frac{1}{3}\ln|x^3 - 1| + C$

53 $\ln|\sin x| + C$ **54** $-\ln|\cos x| + C$

55 $-\sqrt{1 - x^2} + C$ **56** $\frac{-1}{2(n+1)}(1 - x^2)^{n+1} + C$

57 $2\sqrt{1 + 2x} + C$ **58** $2\sqrt{3 + 2x^2} + C$

59 $2\sqrt{\sin x} + C$ **60** $2\sqrt{1 + e^x} + C$

61 $-\frac{1}{2}\sqrt{1 - x^4} + C$ **62** $\sqrt{2x^2 + x^4} + C$

63 $\frac{2\sqrt{3}}{3}x^{\frac{3}{2}} + C$ **64** $\frac{2}{\sqrt{2}}x^{\frac{1}{2}} + C$ or $\sqrt{2x} + C$

65 $\frac{3^{\frac{4}{3}}}{4}x^{\frac{4}{3}} + C$ **66** $\frac{1}{2}\ln|x| + C$ or $\ln|\sqrt{x}| + C$

67 $(2 + \cos x)^{-1} + C$ **68** $\frac{1}{8}(1 + 2\sin x)^4 + C$

69 $\frac{1}{2}\ln|3 + 2\sin x| + C$ **70** $2\sqrt{1 + e^x} + C$

Exercise 8, page 39

1 $\frac{1}{2}x + \frac{1}{4}\sin 2x + C$ **2** $\frac{1}{2}x - \frac{1}{2}\sin x + C$

3 $\tan x + C$ **4** $-x - \cot x + C$

5 $\ln|\sin x| + C$ **6** $\frac{1}{2}x + \frac{1}{8}\sin 4x + C$

7 $-\cot x + C$ **8** $\frac{3}{8}x - \frac{1}{4}\sin 2x + \frac{1}{32}\sin 4x + C$

9 $\sqrt{2} \sin x + C$

10 $\frac{1}{2} \sin^2 x + C \ or \ -\frac{1}{2} \cos^2 x + C$

11 $-\frac{1}{3} \cos 3x - \cos x + C$

12 $\frac{1}{12} \sin 6x + \frac{1}{4} \sin 2x + C$

13 $\frac{1}{4} \sin 2x - \frac{1}{8} \sin 4x + C$

14 $\frac{1}{2} \cos 2x - \frac{1}{6} \cos 6x + C$

15 $2 \ln|x-1| + \ln|x+1| + C$

16 $3 \ln|x-3| + 2 \ln|x+2| + C$

17 $\ln|4x-3| - \ln|2x+1| + C$

18 $\ln|2x+1| + \ln|3x-1| + C$

19 $2 \ln|x+1| - \dfrac{3}{x+1} + C$

20 $\ln|2x-1| - \dfrac{1}{2(2x-1)} + C$

21 $\frac{3}{2} \ln|2x-5| - \dfrac{1}{(2x-5)} + C$

22 $\ln|x+2| + \dfrac{2}{(x+2)} + C$

23 $x + \frac{1}{2} \ln|x+1| + \frac{1}{2} \ln|x-1| + C$

24 $x + \ln|x-2| - \ln|x+2| + C$

25 $x - 2 \ln|x+1| - \dfrac{2}{x+1} + C$

26 $x + \frac{4}{5} \ln|x-2| - \frac{9}{5} \ln|x+3| + C$

Exercise 9, page 47

1 $\frac{2}{5}(x-3)^{\frac{5}{2}} + 2(x-3)^{\frac{3}{2}} + C$

2 $\frac{2}{5}(x-2)^{\frac{5}{2}} + \frac{8}{3}(x-2)^{\frac{3}{2}} + C$

3 $\frac{1}{10}(2x+1)^{\frac{5}{2}} - \frac{1}{6}(2x+1)^{\frac{3}{2}} + C$

4 $\frac{1}{5}(2x-3)^{\frac{5}{2}} + \frac{2}{3}(2x-3)^{\frac{3}{2}} + C$

5 $\frac{2}{45}(3x+2)^{\frac{5}{2}} + \frac{4}{27}(3x+2)^{\frac{3}{2}} + C$

6 $\frac{1}{28}(2x+1)^{\frac{7}{2}} - \frac{1}{10}(2x+1)^{\frac{5}{2}} + \frac{1}{12}(2x+1)^{\frac{3}{2}} + C$

7 $(1+2x)^{\frac{1}{2}} + C$

8 $\frac{1}{3}\left(1+x^2\right)^{\frac{3}{2}} - \left(1+x^2\right)^{\frac{1}{2}} + C$

9 $-\left(9-x^2\right)^{\frac{1}{2}} + C$

10 $\sin^{-1}\left(\frac{1}{3}x\right) + C$

11 $\frac{1}{2}\left(4+x^2\right) - 2\ln\left(4+x^2\right) + C$

12 $\frac{1}{2}\tan^{-1}\left(\frac{1}{2}x\right) + C$

13 $\frac{2}{5}(x+1)^{\frac{5}{2}} - \frac{2}{3}(x+1)^{\frac{3}{2}} + C$

14 $\frac{1}{5}(2x-3)^{\frac{5}{2}} + (2x-3)^{\frac{3}{2}} + C$

15 $\frac{2}{9}\left(3x^2-2\right)^{\frac{3}{2}} + C$

16 $\frac{1}{40}(4x+3)^{\frac{5}{2}} + \frac{5}{24}(4x+3)^{\frac{3}{2}} + C$

17 $\frac{2}{3}(2+3x)^{\frac{1}{2}} + C$

18 $\frac{2}{3}(3-x)^{\frac{3}{2}} - 6(3-x)^{\frac{1}{2}} + C$

19 $\sin^{-1} x + C$

20 $\frac{1}{5}\tan^{-1}\left(\frac{1}{5}x\right) + C$

21 $\frac{1}{2}\ln\left(25+x^2\right) + C$

22 $x - 5\tan^{-1}\left(\frac{1}{5}x\right) + C$

23 $-\frac{1}{2}\sqrt{3-x^2} + C$

24 $\sin^{-1}\dfrac{x}{\sqrt{3}} + C$

25	0 and $\frac{1}{6}\pi$	**26**	1 and 0
27	0 and $\frac{1}{4}\pi$	**28**	3 and 4
29	0 and $\tan^{-1}\frac{1}{3}$	**30**	-3 and -2
31	$\frac{1}{6}\pi$	**32**	$\frac{14}{15}$
33	$\frac{1}{8}\pi$	**34**	$4\sqrt{3}-6\frac{2}{3}$
35	$1-3\tan^{-1}\frac{1}{3}$	**36**	$21\frac{2}{3}-54\ln\frac{3}{2}$

Exercise 10, page 53

1 $x\sin x+\cos x+C$

2 $\frac{1}{2}xe^{2x}-\frac{1}{4}e^{2x}+C$

3 $\frac{1}{2}x\sin 2x+\frac{1}{4}\cos 2x+C$

4 $-xe^{-2x}-\frac{1}{2}e^{-2x}+C$

5 $\frac{1}{2}x^2\ln x-\frac{1}{4}x^2+C$

6 $-x^2\cos x+2x\sin x+2\cos x+C$

7 $-x^2e^{-x}-2xe^{-x}-2e^{-x}+C$

8 $\frac{1}{3}x^3\ln x-\frac{1}{9}x^3+C$

9 $\frac{1}{2}(\ln x)^2+C$

10 $\frac{1}{2}x^2\sin 2x+\frac{1}{2}x\cos 2x-\frac{1}{4}\sin 2x+C$

11 $-\dfrac{x}{a}e^{-xa}-\dfrac{1}{a^2}e^{-xa}+C$

12 $\frac{1}{2}x-\frac{1}{2}\sin x\cos x+C$

13 $x\sin^{-1}x+\sqrt{1-x^2}+C$

14 $\frac{1}{2}x^2\tan^{-1}x+\frac{1}{2}\tan^{-1}x-\frac{1}{2}x+C$

15 $x\tan^{-1}x-\frac{1}{2}\ln\left(1+x^2\right)+C$

16 $\frac{2}{3}x^{\frac{3}{2}}\ln x-\frac{4}{9}x^{\frac{3}{2}}+C$

17 $\frac{1}{2}e^x\sin x+\frac{1}{2}e^x\cos x+C$

18 $\dfrac{a}{a^2+b^2}e^{xa}\sin bx-\dfrac{b}{a^2+b^2}e^{xa}\cos bx+C$

Exercise 11, page 58

1 e^3-e

2 $\frac{1}{2}\pi$

3 $3\ln 2-1$

4 $\frac{1}{2}\ln 5$

5 $\frac{1}{2}\left(1-\dfrac{1}{e^9}\right)$

6 $-\ln 18$

7 $\frac{1}{2}\pi$

8 $\frac{1}{2}\pi^2$

9 $\frac{1}{2}\pi\left(e^2-\dfrac{1}{e^2}\right)$

10 $\pi\left(16(\ln 2)^2-16\ln 2+6\right)$

11 $\dfrac{1}{6}\pi^2 + \dfrac{\sqrt{3}}{4}\pi$ **12** $\tan^{-1}\!\left(\tfrac{1}{2}\right)$

13 $1 - \dfrac{2}{e}$ **14** $1 - \dfrac{1}{e}$

15 $\pi\!\left(1 - \tfrac{1}{4}\pi\right)$

Exercise 12, page 63

Four sets of answers are given, the first for the rectangle rule, then the trapezoidal rule, the mid-point rule, and finally for Simpson's rule. In each case, the answers are given correct to six decimal places, but that does not indicate the accuracy you can expect.

The rectangle rule.

1	0.202 5	**2**	1.091 622
3	0.919 403	**4**	1.106 657
5	2.507 707	**6**	7.741 407

The trapezoidal rule

1	0.252 5	**2**	1.112 332
3	0.997 943	**4**	1.185 197
5	2.578 704	**6**	8.147 741

The mid-point rule

1	0.248 75	**2**	1.111 006
3	1.001 029	**4**	1.201 932
5	2.576 424	**6**	8.144 793

Simpson's rule

1	0.25	**2**	1.111 446
3	1.000 003	**4**	1.193 089
5	2.577 184	**6**	8.145 797

Exercise 13, page 67

1 $y = Ce^{\frac{1}{2}x}$ **2** $y = Ce^{-x}$

3 $y = Ce^{\frac{1}{2}x^2}$ **4** $y = Ce^{-\frac{1}{2}x^2}$

5 $\sin y + \cos x = C$ **6** $e^y = \tfrac{1}{2}x^2 + C$

7 $y = Cx^2$
9 $y = 3x + 2$
8 $\cos y = C \cos x$
10 $y = -x - 3$
11 $y = 1 + e^{\frac{1}{2}x^2}$ or $y = 1 - e^{\frac{1}{2}x^2}$
12 $y = 2x^2$
13 $\ln\left|y^2 - 1\right| = e^x - 1$
14 $y^2 = 20x + 900$
15 $\sin y = 2 \sin x$
16 $y = \frac{2}{5}x^{\frac{5}{2}} - \frac{2}{3}x^{\frac{3}{2}}$

Exercise 14, page 72

1 $x^2 + y^2 = 25$
2 $y = 2x$
3 21 minutes
4 $q = 1000e^{-t \ln 2}$
5 $\frac{3}{2} - \frac{3}{2}\cos 2t$
6 33 minutes
7 $N = \dfrac{1000M}{\left\{1000 + (M - 1000)e^{-Mkt}\right\}}$

Revision exercise 1, page 74

1 $\frac{3}{2}x^2 + x + C$, $\frac{1}{5}x^5 + \frac{2}{3}x^3 + x + C$, $\frac{2}{3}x^{\frac{3}{2}} + C$
2 $y = x^2 + x - 3$
3 66
4 $32\frac{1}{2}\pi$
5 $y = 2x^2$
6 $\left(5\frac{1}{2} - \frac{1}{2}\cos 2\right)$ m, $(2 + \sin 2)$ m s^{-1}

Revision exercise 2, page 74

1 $\frac{1}{12}\sin^2 6x + \frac{1}{2}x + C$, $\frac{1}{4}x^4 + \frac{3}{2}x^2 + 3\ln x - \frac{1}{2}x^{-2} + C$, $\sqrt{2x} + C$
2 $y = \left(3x^2 + 3x + 9\right)^{\frac{1}{3}}$
3 $\frac{1}{15}$
4 $11\frac{1}{4}$
5 $\sqrt{18}$ m s^{-1}
6 $7\frac{1}{8}\pi$

Revision exercise 3, page 75

1 $1, 2, \ln 4$

2 $0 \text{ m s}^{-1}, 1200 \text{ m}$

3 $\ln y = \sin x - x \cos x - 1$, $e^{\pi - 1}$

4 $\frac{2}{5}\pi, \frac{5}{14}\pi$

5 $2\ln 2 - \frac{5}{4}$

6 $\dfrac{a e^{ax} \sin bx - b e^{ax} \cos bx}{a^2 + b^2} + C$

Revision exercise 4, page 75

1 $\frac{1}{3}, \frac{7}{24}, \frac{1}{2}\pi$

2 $v = \dfrac{g\left(1 - e^{-kt}\right)}{k}$

3 $\frac{1}{12}$

4 $\frac{1}{10}\pi$

5 $y = \frac{1}{2}\left(1 + x^2\right)$

6 $\frac{14}{15}\sqrt{2} - \frac{1}{15}$

Revision exercise 5, page 76

1 $1, \frac{3}{16} - \frac{1}{8}\ln 2, \frac{1}{2}\ln 2$

2 $\frac{1}{6}(b - a)^3$

3 $\frac{1}{2}\pi^2$

4 $y = \sqrt{1 - 2\sqrt{\left(1 - x^2\right)}}$

5 $\dfrac{e^{n+1}}{n+1} - \dfrac{e^{n+1}}{(n+1)^2} + \dfrac{1}{(n+1)^2}$

6 $\sqrt{\dfrac{g\left(1 - e^{-2kx}\right)}{k}}$

Revision exercise 6, page 76

1 $\frac{1}{2}\pi$, $24\frac{1}{5}$, $\frac{1}{2}-\frac{1}{2}\ln 2$

2 $2^{\frac{1}{5}}$

3 $4\frac{1}{2}$

4 $\frac{1}{3}\ln\left(2+3e^{2x}\right)+C$

5 $\dfrac{5\ln\frac{5}{2}}{\ln\frac{5}{3}}\approx 8.97$ min

6 $y=-\frac{3}{2}-\frac{1}{2}e^{2x}$

Revision exercise 7, page 77

1 -1, π, $\frac{1}{2}\ln 5$

2 $\sin^{-1}\dfrac{2x}{\sqrt{3}}+C$

3 $\frac{10}{3}\sqrt{5}-2\sqrt{3}$

4 8π

5 $y^2=1+2x^2$

6 $v=\pm 2\sqrt{\left(1-x^3\right)}$

Index